CINNAMON TWIST

Louisa Berry

GW00771956

3P
PUBLISHING

CINNAMON TWIST

Copyright © 3P Publishing
First published in 2018 in the UK
3P Publishing
C E C, London Road
Corby
NN17 5EU

A catalogue number for this book is available from
the British Library

ISBN: 978-1-911559-83-2
Cover design: Jamie Rae
Cover photography by Alan R Horten

CINNAMON TWIST

With lots of lust,

Louisa

X

CINNAMON TWIST

CINNAMON TWIST

To all those who thought "fuck it" and did it anyway. Life is for living after all.

CINNAMON TWIST

Contents:

CINNAMON TWIST

Acknowledgments

So quickly after writing Vanilla Extract, we now have Cinnamon Twist and many of the people I thanked before should be thanked again, but that wouldn't make for too exciting reading for the avid reader.

This time round, with a few followers on various social media, I would like to thank those who have stuck by me, not sent me cock shots, nor declared their love or asked for the phone number of the model on my book covers! Instead, they have respected that I am an author and not a dating app, and to those I'd like to say thank you.

My huge appreciation goes to Alan Horten, who again took some wonderful images, and they are displayed either side of this book. Not only is Alan an inspiration behind the camera but also a very good friend. I hear his neighbours also enjoy the photo shoots!

To my beautiful children I thank for their love and support, even if it did mean some awkward questions. I love you dearly – always will!

Thank you to the new people you will soon meet in the following pages, for allowing me to share their stories. The names are changed where they asked me to and left the same where they preferred the limelight. It seems a bit of fame goes a long way on Tinder (just ask Pearls of Wisdom)!

Louisa Berry

CINNAMON TWIST

CINNAMON TWIST

Prologue

Since the separation and subsequent divorce from her husband, Lou's journey of self and sexual discovery began with a vengeance. She had enjoyed a number of very intimate encounters that she would always remember. Some of those were good, some fantastic and others she would quite happily forget. Despite the thrills and the previously unimaginable mind-blowing experiences, Lou found that even with all that excitement, she was left feeling unfulfilled. Was this her life now, going from one sexual liaison to another? Was this now the norm? When would she ever be truly satisfied? Why did she always seem to feel she was missing out?

Lou was not the kind of woman to be without male company for long. She never had been. Lou had always had a high sex drive, and even though she decided to hang up her swinging boots, she continued to stay in touch with some men she had 'played' with before. It was less than a handful, but it meant she still had the variety when she needed it and, importantly, it was absolutely on her terms and just how she liked it.

What Lou had found was that any man she gave her 100% attention to (even for a short while), soon turned from being a strong, masculine and passionate lover, to a crumbling mess before her eyes. Sex for Lou was all-encompassing and all giving (and taking). There were no half measures. Why would there be? If you had got as far as getting naked and sharing fluids, why would you not give it all you had? Sadly, some men interpreted that as them being the only male in her life; the only person she could possibly have that connection with and feel that special with, which was not the case. Furthermore, this sent them into a frenzy about keeping her attention, and usually, this took the form of over-complimenting her. Lou surmised that some women would adore this praise and adoration – she did herself to a certain extent, but when it became over-powering and soppy, she found it an instant turn off. It showed their desperation and weakness, which would invariably lead to them having to go. Rather than please her, as was the intention, it aggravated her and turned her completely off them.

With that in mind, Lou was not quite sure she was ready to be tamed, but if a decent relationship came along, 'vanilla' or otherwise, then it might just be worth taking a gamble. Maybe this was her time to have a 'rock' and not just the one between a man's legs.

Chapter 1 - Adventure time

One of the 'regulars' who Lou saw roughly every three months seemed to be the one she found herself calling upon most frequently while she absented herself from the online sex site she subscribed to. Brad was intelligent, fit and treated her like a princess. In fact, he was the only one ever to buy her flowers and this was very special to her. He also just so happened to have a huge, thick penis, which she adored, and the sex was on another level.

So when Brad told her that he didn't want to be 'one of her many,' Lou was rather surprised and wasn't quite sure how to handle it. He wanted to be her only one and for them to have a go at being monogamous. Lou took some time to contemplate how this would work. She was curious to have a normal relationship again but wasn't convinced she was ready for it. What if she got itchy feet again? What if she missed the buzz of meeting new people and being in control of her insatiable sexual appetite? And ultimately, as she had found in the past, would she get bored?

Lou did have a good think about it, and the two of them spoke for hours on the terms. Initially, Lou said no because she wasn't 100% certain. It wasn't that she didn't think they were compatible. She knew they fit perfectly and they had a great time together - every time. He challenged her mentally, and this was a turn on in itself. What she really didn't want to do was hurt him, and she could already see he was getting emotionally attached. She was worried it could end badly and she didn't want to put him through any pain. He was too lovely for that and had suffered rejection a number of times already in his forty years.

Brad was saddened when she turned him down, and his only reaction was to withdraw. There was no way he could continue with the current set up, as it was already causing him conflict. Lou was also upset. They'd built up a very close friendship during their time together, so it was a real shame to leave it there. Brad said he owed it to himself to walk away, as he had to respect himself. Lou completely understood and agreed, and this increased her levels of respect for him.

A few quiet weeks passed, and Lou found she was missing him, even though her other regulars were serving her needs sexually. She decided to send him a smiley kiss face on Whatsapp and he responded instantly. It transpired that Brad had missed her too, but they were both unsure how to approach each other. "How about we give this a go then?" she asked him. His glee was apparent, and he jumped into his car to head straight over to Lou's house immediately. A celebration was in order!

Five months of a mostly happy relationship passed and during this time they had some amazing adventures; being spontaneous and visiting swinging clubs and parties at a number of UK locations. Given Brad had been in the swinging scene much longer, around ten years, he had a much better understanding of how it all worked, but he was also very sceptical of some of the key players and their intentions. He was quick to point out how single females were being used, becoming 'free whores' for other party guests and how single men were providing their payment to the organisers by handing over extortionate entrance fees.

This was a different perspective than Lou had ever considered. She was unaware of any underlying methods and practices, but she could see where he was coming from. She did point out though that this was all through choice and everyone involved decided themselves whether to participate or not. No one was being forced into this. The single men and women could choose not to attend if they didn't want to. It was entirely their decision (unless something way more sinister was afoot).

Brad introduced a few doubts into Lou's mind, and not all of them were founded on the truth, in her eyes. At the outset of their relationship, they agreed they would swap partners in a club situation, on the proviso that both members of the couple would be attractive and worthy of having sex with them. Lou should have known this was a smokescreen, as it proved harder and harder to find such a couple no matter how many parties or clubs they attended. It seemed that finding a beautiful couple they both wanted to have sex with was nigh on impossible. Either that or he was just putting barriers in the way whenever she suggested any potential pairings.

Brad was one of the many men who agreed that

an FFM (female, female, male) would be ultra-hot, but he was not so keen on a MMF (male, male, female). He did admit this was unfair on her, and Lou wasn't convinced she agreed with his reasoning. "The third party in an MMF is always trying to out-do the husband or boyfriend. They want to give her something better than she's already got." Lou didn't agree. Her counter argument was that a young guy would be out to prove himself, but given they were in their 40's, and with a higher level of maturity, the guy would be there purely to have fun. "But I've been that third party, and I know how it works." Lou still didn't agree. She'd had a few MMFs in her time and found there was no trying to be the better man sexually in any of those set-ups. He was bullshitting her and she knew it.

The only time they did play with another couple was on holiday. They attended a swingers club and found a very beautiful couple that asked to join them. They were in their late thirties and were both incredibly attractive, athletic, well-dressed and smelled delicious. Lou and the lady began kissing passionately at the bar and were soon caressing each other wantonly. They all decided to move to the open bedded area rather swiftly, and the fun began.

Both women removed their dresses, revealing their sumptuous underwear beneath, and cast their shoes aside. Interestingly and with the essence of a more youthful body, her new playmate's two set was probably the same size as her own, but Lou's 34D cup seemed somewhat less perky. There was no way the other lady had breastfed four beautiful babies - one at most (if any). Her stomach was tight too,

6

and unlike Lou, there was no excess skin hanging anywhere over the top edge of the size ten knickers! It was all very athletic and tidy. She really was beautiful. But none of this was important. There were far more fun things to be thinking about right now.

Crawling onto the bed, none of the shooting thoughts through Lou's head mattered. They had been instant assessments. Kneeling in front of her, Lou resumed their tender kissing and touching. What the men were getting up to, they had no idea. They were absorbed in their girl on girl play, and it wasn't important what the others were doing. They were savouring each delightfully tingly caress.

It was apparent the couple did not speak much English, so Lou gestured for her to lie down with her and she soon began to devour her body. She continued her kisses before concentrating on her neck. Nuzzling into it, she pecked it softly and made her way down to her voluptuous breasts. They were magnificent and natural, and they needed to be freed. Lou unbuttoned the red silk bra and released them to her care. Lou couldn't help but fondle them. Squeezing and sucking, they felt amazingly firm in her hands and her mouth – delicious. The effect was electric for both ladies, as her newly found friend wriggled in delight and Lou's pussy grew ever wetter.

Her body was fantastic - toned and tanned all over; Lou enjoyed exploring it. She made her way down and removed her matching knickers. They were also damp and gave away her levels of arousal. Carefully putting them to one side with the bra, Lou placed one hand on each thigh and spread her legs apart. Kneeling and facing her prey, Lou noticed how her pussy was glistening before her. Lou gently began to flick her tongue upon it and commence her feast.

These very friendly females were completely absorbed in the moment, and it was only when Lou felt a nudge behind her, that she realised Brad was there. He was naked, and his cock was solid against her. It took little guiding as Lou was already so excited and in it slid to her loud moan. Thank goodness they didn't use condoms any more. Everything was so much more sensitive without them. He did have a tremendous penis and one that hit the spot every single time in whatever position, angle, anything. It felt divine as he took her from behind and she continued to pleasure her *amiga,* who was now masturbating her partner at the same time, before taking his hard cock into her mouth.

Soon after, the Spanish couple mirrored their doggy style opposite them, allowing the ladies to continue kissing at the same time. It was a super-hot setup, and it was obvious that this couple ticked all their pre-agreed requirements for a full swap. Lou thought that would be the natural progression, as they were all so comfortable with each other. However, Brad wasn't having any of it. When she indicated that they should change the dynamics, he showed no signs of wanting to. Lou made it clear she wanted to switch partners, but Brad had other ideas and continued to fuck Lou on the bed instead, not letting her go. This was not the worst thing in the world as he was an incredible shag, but she had hoped for some variation tonight, as she had on a few occasions recently.

This was a clear indication to Lou that Brad had not been entirely truthful with her. The warning signs were there, and Lou knew their time together was becoming limited. They had enjoyed their summer together; being each other's confidant, support and ear to chew (as well as nether regions), but it was time to call it a day.

There was definitely a moment earlier on in their relationship where Lou felt she was falling for Brad. He was certainly a match to her intellectual level, and he challenged her on many things that had enriched their relationship further. He was adventurous, a lot of fun to be around and they often spoke for hours on end about all different aspects of life as well as the swinging scene. She trusted him, and that meant a lot. It had been some time since she'd let anyone in that close.

When the voices appeared in her head, mimicking his sayings, she knew he wasn't the one after all. His over-inflated sense of self-sanctimony made Lou realise that she was better off on her own. While the sex had been tremendous, and riding bareback was a sensual novelty, there were more exciting times to be had elsewhere, without Brad.

It was not particularly an easy break, but he kept to his word, and once he was gone, he never returned. It would be too painful for any reconciliation, and she didn't want to cause him any more upset. As time went on, Lou wondered if he'd changed his views at all, but doubted it. He was very forthright and stubborn - much like her really. Maybe they were too alike?

CINNAMON TWIST

So Princess Lou put herself back on the market and was decidedly keen not to miss out on anything else. She wasn't sure how many frogs she'd have to kiss to find her true love, but she was certainly ready to make a start on her next adventures.

Chapter 2: Sharp dressed man

"Hi again. We've still not arranged to meet up yet. I'm often at a loose end in London and would love to meet you." Well, that was a very nice line to reconnect with Lou, even if she couldn't actually remember who he was. Of late, she had been inundated on the website, to the point where she'd lost track of how many guys and couples she was talking to. Lou also remembered this was a cycle. Having been on and off this crazy sex site, she knew that it could be all-consuming if she let it and how very easy it was to become embroiled in it again.

Lou took another look at his profile. She couldn't see his face, but his body was fit enough. 'Mmmm,' she thought. 'He looks rather delicious.' This was confirmed when she looked at the photos he'd attached to the message. 'Ooh, what a cutie!' Described as 'blond, six feet two inches, athletic build, horny and wanting to try new things.' Lou was sure she could find some sort of way to help him out.

Lou responded, "Well it sounds like it is overdue. When are you next free?" Unfortunately, Warren was out of the country on business for the weekend ahead, so Lou would have to wait a little longer to meet up. This was not a problem, but something in their follow up conversations led to

Lou's intrigue growing about this rather handsome man, and she became quite keen in wanting to find out more about him.

After her children had gone to bed that Saturday night, Lou found herself sipping on a glass of red wine and wondering about Warren. What was it he did for a living that led him to stay so often in London and had him jetting off for weekends away? (Not that Lou had any idea if this trip was for business or pleasure.) The mystery of this man needed solving.

Lou decided to leave him a message. It was probably the wine that helped with the construction of her approach. "What a shame you're away. Maybe I should have come with you?" 'Ah fuck it,' she thought. 'Nothing to lose.' She left her mobile number and suggested they spoke on Whatsapp when he returned. Lou knew it would be a few days before Warren was back in the UK and doubted she would hear from him until then.

Lou enjoyed the rest of her weekend and didn't log onto the site until after work on Monday. She had a sparkle in her eye when she saw Warren's message waiting for her. "Yes, that was a shame. You would have had a great time. When are you free? I really can't wait to meet you. It's been so long! Let me know if it's ok to message you off of here." Lou was beaming from ear to ear. Polite, respectful, gorgeous; what was the catch? She wrote back and confirmed it was fine to message now, and within three minutes the arrangements were starting to be made.

CINNAMON TWIST

Lunch the following Wednesday was the plan. Warren would travel across London to Canary Wharf, and the restaurant choice was left with Lou, as he was not familiar with the area. Lou toyed with a few different options, in a completely selfish manner. Did she want Japanese, which could be tricky to eat gracefully, and she didn't really know her way around the menu? Should they go for noodles, but they could be even messier? Lou found that usually, unexplained splash spots would miraculously appear on any white or cream item of clothing following such a meal, and that was certainly not the look she was going for when they met. Would a burger be too boring? So many to choose from! In the end, she went with a Scottish steak and fish restaurant. It was close to where he would be landing on the Docklands Light Railway, and Lou had always found the standards of food and service to be very high there.

Their messaging on the day became quite childlike. Both appeared to be somewhat excited. Some rapid messages were fired in the build-up to the lunch, ever increasing as 12:30 approached. Lou asked him to 'ping her' when his train arrived at Limehouse station, so she could descend the always busy lifts in work and be at the Canary Wharf stop for his arrival. Unfortunately, Warren didn't receive this notification until he had already arrived, catching Lou a little off-guard as he messaged, "I'm here." Lou's heart raced. Why was she so nervous about this meet? She'd had a few 'socials' lately and hadn't been in the slightest bit phased before any of them. Maybe it was because Warren oozed class and

13

sex appeal. Lou had a feeling this was going to be something special.

"What can you see?" she asked as she walked along the busy shopping mall. Warren was outside a shirt shop. "Don't move. I'll come and get you," and that's exactly what Lou did. A minute or two later Lou spied Warren standing a level up from where she was. From what she could see, he looked immaculately dressed in a three-piece navy suit. Instantly the old ZZ Top song filled her head! She couldn't wait to examine him up close.

Appearing to be calm when inside the anticipation was building to the point of overflowing, she stepped onto the escalator and at the same time messaged him, "I can see you." She noticed he hadn't read it though, as she walked towards him. To her surprise, Warren was already walking towards her, with a massive smile on his face, exposing great teeth (which could always be a deal-breaker for Lou). "Hello young lady," he greeted her. He looked super excited too and gave her a kiss on the cheek. "Hello you," she said, smiling as well. He was incredibly handsome, and inside her head, Lou gave an imaginary fist pump.

"So where are you taking me?" Warren asked. "How do you fancy steak?" Grinning and nodding at the same time, it was an affirmative. Intentionally bumping their shoulders together, they set off. It was only a short walk away, and soon they were sat next to the window overlooking the Cabot Square fountains. Despite it being a somewhat grey day, it felt like the sun was shining brightly on these two eager individuals.

Their conversation was constant and without any gaps. Lou was finding him fascinating – to speak with but also to look at. He did have a beautiful face, almost David Beckham-like, with some soft blond stubble. He had a full head of slicked-back hair, and he radiated class. 'Damn this guy is hot,' Lou thought. He told her she was way better than her profile photographs. "You have got a fantastic smile and if you don't mind me saying, a great set of legs." Lou was appreciative of his praise, being a sucker for attention as she was. He was a charmer, that was for sure, and she loved it. He could keep that up for as long as he liked during this delightful lunch.

They chose the same dishes, which were delicious, and both laughed at the portion sizes of the vegetables as they came out. Funnily enough, though, they didn't get finished, so it seemed the restaurant had a better idea than they did on how much food they needed.

Lou was surprised to find, as with their messaging, that they were almost finishing each other's sentences. There had been many occasions in the past two weeks of corresponding that they had said the same thing at the same time. As Warren was typing it, Lou was thinking it, and vice versa. It was spooky how quickly they had become in sync, and at lunch, it was no different. A couple of times one or the other would have to stop talking because it was obvious they were both thinking exactly the same thing.

They soon turned their dialogue to personal experiences of people they had met on the site; the good encounters and the less so. Both had some stories in either category, and each enjoyed recalling some of those. It was a very funny hour and a half. They fed off each other – not literally, but with the witty reminiscing and longing to know more. The two older gentlemen in grey suits on the table next to them certainly appeared to be enjoying their conversation too. At times it looked like they were straining to hear. Lou and Warren's topics were far more interesting than their own business discussions it seemed.

One thing that resonated with Lou was when Warren revealed his birthday. It seemed they shared the same zodiac sign, and with it being the sexiest of them all, Lou couldn't help but wonder if their intercourse would be as hot as their forecast. It was bound to be!

Lunch went all too quickly for Lou's liking. She could happily have sat there all afternoon. They had a lot in common, and it was a real shame they had to return to work. 'Damn that work getting in the way,' Lou thought to herself.

In the lift down from the restaurant, Lou was itching to kiss him. They were standing close, but for some reason, given he was in his pristine suit and she was so smartly dressed too, it felt a little out of place just to launch herself at his face and body – though it was very tempting. Instead, business composure remained, and they both departed for their separate onward journeys: his by Docklands Light Railway and hers just a short walk to her building. A kiss was firmly planted on each other's cheeks as they said goodbye. Lou had a glowing smile across her face as she strode back to the office.

She was full of confidence and had an air of mischief too.

The following night Lou had previously pencilled in a social meeting with someone else, but she had decided at lunch today that her arrangements would definitely be changing. Warren had confirmed he was available and apparently had a plan he wanted to share with her about that evening. 'This all sounds rather intriguing,' Lou thought. He certainly had sparked her interest, and she couldn't wait to see him again.

The messaging continued that afternoon and evening. Lou's children were home and after returning from work, cooking dinner, clearing up, soaking briefly in the bath and 'de-fuzzing' all bodily hair she no longer required, Lou then finally relaxed.

Warren provided instructions on how he saw the evening going, and it went a little something like this:

1. They would meet at Waterloo underground station, (next to the cake stall) where they would go for a coffee or something stronger.

2. On then to his hotel, they would deposit their bags, coats and anything else they did not require.

3. Head down to the sauna and steam rooms in the hotel for some pampering.

4. She would be treated to a massage a la Warren.

5. Dinner would then follow.

Well, that sounded like a perfect way to unwind after work on a Thursday. Lou wondered if they would make it any further than number two above? She could foresee it being difficult to leave his hotel room once they had gone inside. They were bound to kiss. Things would get heated and they would be unlikely to go anywhere else. If Lou understood gambling, which she didn't, she would have put money on that being the sequence of events, with the ultimate outcome. But, as it transpired, she would have lost that bet.

They met at Waterloo as planned, although with that many exits Warren was bound to miss her, and he did. Thank goodness for mobile phones. She messaged him her location, and he told her to stop where she was. "Don't move," he said (repeating the process from their lunch the day before). "I'm coming to get you." Lou smiled like a child, full of joy. He really was intelligent and funny.

Lou's overnight bag consisted of a small rucksack. There wasn't much she needed. She had worked from home that day and only came into London to see him. As the next day was 'dress-down Friday' in the office, her chosen attire was a little less corporate this evening. She would be working in those skin-tight black jeans tomorrow, so she took it up a gear by wearing a pair of black leather peep-toe ankle boots. At four inches high, they would still accentuate her legs, and he was a 'leg man' after all. Their shape wouldn't be lost under the jeans.

Standing put under Waterloo railway, looking at The Royal Festival Hall, Lou patiently waited for him to arrive. He wasn't far away. He had told her he would change out of his suit beforehand to match her style, so she wasn't entirely sure what he would be wearing when he arrived. She desperately hoped it would not be the standard slacks, shirt and jumper around the shoulders, worse still those suede boating shoes in navy. Lou knew the latter were probably stupidly expensive, but they just did nothing for her, and the last thing she wanted was to be embarrassed by what he had on.

There was no need to worry. Lou was not disappointed. The rather lovely man coming towards her as she stood waiting was wearing a skinny pair of black jeans, with a polo shirt and denim jacket. Even casual he looked hot and again was adorning the customary huge grin. It was seconds before they were both smiling and the non-stop chatting started up once more.

Warren threw Lou by asking to take her bag. Lou was genuinely shocked and happily handed it over. What a gent he was! And on to the coffee shop, they ambled.

They found a table outside, and Lou waited there for Warren as he went in to collect the drinks. He made her laugh from afar as she was sitting happily at a table in the warm sunshine waiting for his return. Lou's phone pinged and it was Warren messaging her. It was just a silly comment, but it made her smile just how cute this attractive man could be, and good to know he was thinking of her from inside. There was no real need to be sat there drinking coffee really, but it gave them more time to get to know each other and talk about life in general before continuing with their itinerary. It was like she had known him for years; so relaxed was she in his company and he seemed to be the same too around her.

To his hotel next and Lou was impressed as the lift rode to the 14th floor, where his suite awaited them. Leather sofas to the left as they entered and his range of matching ties and handkerchiefs all strategically placed by the vanity mirror. His attention to detail was impressive.

A small kitchen area opposite the bathroom led into the large bedroom section that had been pristinely cleaned earlier in the day. 'Well this is a bit posh,' she thought. 'Not bad at all.' Obviously she kept that to herself. She didn't want him thinking she was a scally (one of his terms, not hers. It was a northern slang word for 'trailer trash' or similar.) She daren't tell him yet then that she would probably liberate the bathroom toiletries too, but that would come in time!

Warren placed her rucksack on the sofa and removed his denim jacket. Lou took off her coat, and he hung it up for her. Inside the wardrobe she noticed his carefully ironed shirts hanging up next to his suits. There certainly was something about an incredibly smart man. In the quick glance, she saw that they were all colour-coded too. There must be a touch of OCD here. She was sure she'd find out if there were.

Warren went in for the kill. He grabbed the back of her neck and pulled her face close to his. Lou was full of anticipation and desire. She wanted to kiss him too – ever since the post-lunch lift experience the day before. His tongue was cautious as it entered her mouth, but Lou was responsive and eager to welcome him. Her body instantly flinched. (They'd talked about the importance of kissing and their shared dismay of people who took it so lightly. It revealed so much about a person and equally, usually, just how good the sex would be.)

Oh, this certainly felt good. The desire to rip each other's clothes off was powerful. The sexual chemistry was ignited, and Lou doubted they would make it to the sauna at all? Despite the longing, she said, "But we have a plan. Let's stick to the plan." Warren smiled. "You're right. We do have to stick to the plan." She could tell he was thinking the same as her though. All they both really desired was to be naked and fornicating, in what ever shape that took.

"Ok, ok, yes, yes, we should stick to the plan," Warren repeated, almost through gritted teeth. Just then Lou's phone rang. It was her daughter, who she then started to speak with for around ten minutes. During this time, she sat herself down on the stool set up for the vanity mirror. Lou marvelled at the array of accessories as she spoke with her, all the time straddled the stool, which was much to Warren's delight. She had no idea he had been staring at the way she was sitting and even found that a turn on, he would later admit. It was the way her legs looked, opened and in the heeled boots, definitely sexy.

Lou was blissfully unaware until he knelt in front of her and began to kiss her neck. Now she felt it difficult to concentrate on her conversation, but that was, fortunately, coming to a natural conclusion anyway. She ended the call and focused on him. He was kissing her deeply and grinding his groin into hers. It felt tingly and exciting, as every new encounter is with someone Lou didn't really know but wanted to get to know oh so very intimately. She could feel her knickers getting wet as his force was upon her.

It was difficult to break apart, but they knew they had to if they were going to do all the things on their list. They joked as they made their way downstairs to the spa. That did take some self-control, and yes, she would have lost that bet. It took huge resolve and restraint not to stay in that rather inviting hotel room for the rest of the evening.

They were both surprised at just how small the spa facilities were. The whole space was indeed minuscule but with the positive that they did have it to themselves. Lou changed into her best bikini, which was in itself a feat as she rarely wore them any more. She was much more in favour of naked sunbathing where she could. It was a shame too to get out of the sexy underwear she had purposely put on before coming out tonight. She doubted he would even get to see it.

From the changing room Lou made her way to meet Warren in the sauna. It was not her first choice as she was conscious that the dry heat always made her jewellery overheat, which she explained. She wasn't in there long with him when she said she would move next door. The steam room, albeit tiny, was looking more appealing.

They relocated and were now sat on the bench getting hot. It was a more bearable heat, she thought, and they were soon cuddling each other in the steam. Her legs were wrapped around him sideways as he faced the door and their hands were caressing each other as they kissed. They discussed the camera situation and whether they were permissible in such a location. Lou doubted it, but they agreed too that the steam wouldn't allow for any clear pictures anyway.

"So Lou, well done. We stuck to our plan, despite any other thoughts we may have had. Now if you want to head back up any time..." She cut him off. "Now! Let's go now. We did what we said we would. Let's go up now!" There was no point labouring this whole pamper thing. They both knew what they wanted, and it was now!

There was no point changing back into their clothes. ('What a waste of good underwear,' she thought. He wouldn't even see that beautiful matching set that Snake Hips had bought her recently on a trip to Prague. Hey ho - never mind. It meant she could wear it another time.) So instead, they went back up to his room in their damp bathrobes and soggy slippers. Until now she had created all sorts of ideas for how she intended their first naked encounter to play out. This was certainly not in any of those imaginings!

Once inside, Lou popped to the toilet as Warren sat on the bed. He was very relaxed but eager to continue with his plan and give her a good massage. His lavender oil was at the ready for her as she approached the bed. "Lay yourself down," he said, "Naked." The latter he said with an attempted Spanish accent. It made her smile. She had already told him about her 'happy ending' massage with Mr

Fit in Gran Canaria the year before, so it amused her to hear him recollect it. Oh, he was good! She liked his attention to detail.

In all honesty, the massage was not the best she had received, but in fairness, Warren had warned her that it probably wouldn't be. He was bursting to taste and get inside her than perform a head to toe pampering. Lou didn't mind either. She was equally as horny, so when he finished on her back and told her to roll over, she spun over super quick and was ready for him.

"Now where do I begin Lou?" Half expecting him to go straight down on her, Warren surprised her by first kissing her ever so delicately on the lips, leading into a deep exploration of her mouth. He really was a wonderful kisser, and from her mouth, he moved to the left side of her neck and gently nibbled. It sent shivers straight down her spine. This was one of her most sensitive areas, and she adored it receiving such attention.

Next were her breasts. He gave them equal attention as he licked from one to the other and then down the length of her torso to her throbbing clit. Lou was desperate now to have his tongue between her legs. She couldn't take it anymore. She had to have him. Her pussy was beckoning him inside. And there he was. Lou gasped as soon as he connected with her expectant bean. She shuddered from head to foot. The desire was so strong, and he soon nourished her by flicking, touching and pressing down on her. Oh boy, this was just what she needed.

CINNAMON TWIST

Lou could tell he was no stranger at giving oral. His skills were remarkable. It wasn't long before she grabbed the back of his head to draw him down further into her. She was drenched, and the bed was suffering beneath, but that was the last thing on her mind. The rotating and grinding against his tongue was all consuming. Lou knew it wouldn't be long before she exploded all over his face. Moving in rhythm, she gripped him tight. Closer and closer, with circular motions, she shouted, "Yes, yes, I'm gonna cum... YES!" Holy fuck! Lou came so hard, her legs and her stomach began to convulse, like some dying droid on a sci-fi film.

Warren waited for her to relax. "You ok?" He asked her furtively. "Can't talk," Lou tried to reply, but the intense waves were still washing over her, soon followed by equally uncontrollable laughter. She felt euphoric.

Once she had calmed down, a moment of clarity engulfed her. "Don't you find it amazing that you can go from not knowing someone at all, to then being in a hotel room and sharing something so intimate as a mind-blowing orgasm together? It's just nuts. I never even knew you two days ago." Warren laughed. He knew exactly what she meant and said, "It's this crazy world we live in!" 'And thank goodness they did,' she thought.

It was Lou's time to share her oral skills with Warren now. She told him to lie down, which he did, but she could sense his concern and unease, which surprised her, given what they had just experienced together. Lou very tenderly kissed him to help him relax and took her time making her way down his chest. Instantly his right hand came across his body to protect his manhood. This was a first for her. She'd never experienced anyone being so tense when she gave a blowjob before.

Lou tried even harder to make him feel comfortable. She kissed his chest, his belly, then his thighs and took her time getting ever closer to her prize. "What are you doing to me?" Lou didn't understand. She looked up to find Warren pointing to his arms. "You've given me goosebumps all over me. Look at my legs too." He was right. Warren was covered from head to foot. "Do you want me to stop?" She asked. Lou was determined to please him, but she wanted to confirm he was enjoying it. "No. I want you to carry on, but I find it really hard to stay calm." Lou reassured him with, "You can trust me. I'll be gentle," and of course she was.

Lou took her time to caress him delicately. She slowly licked either side of his cock and stroked his balls with her tongue. Warren's right hand did wander in from time to time in defence, but it didn't come to rest. It hovered just in case but found it wasn't necessary to protect his penis. She wasn't going to hurt him, and when Lou did finally take him into her mouth, she was very considerate.

Lou would normally and quite literally make a meal of going down on a man. On this occasion, she gave enough stimulation to make Warren want her more. He was already a tingly mess all over. She didn't want to send him over the edge just yet. At that precise moment, Lou decided to set herself an own personal goal; she would make Warren enjoy her oral, no matter how many times it took her, which of course was no burden (to either of them she hoped)! He would learn to relax with her and let Lou do whatever she desired to please him.

"I think you should relax now," he told her. There were no objections. Lou moved to the top of the bed and onto her back. He kissed her again before reaching across to the side table and grabbed a condom. It was soon in place, and he was above her, looking down at the anticipation on her face. The intensity was immense as he slowly entered her body, maintaining eye contact throughout. 'Mmmm, here we go,' she thought. This was going to be a night to remember.

Warren wasn't the biggest man she'd slept with, but the kink in his cock was rubbing inside, just at the right place. 'Size really isn't everything,' Lou thought, as she was beginning to tingle from deep within. "It's just there in the front with you, isn't it?" Warren said. He must have been thinking something similar. "Just there is perfect," Lou said, enjoying each motion. He also happened to look exceptionally hot above her.

Given his slight nervousness with her earlier, Lou decided not to take control and demand to ride him, well not just yet anyway. She would let him take the lead, as that was where he appeared to feel most comfortable. She also had a feeling that they would become regular 'buddies' given they were so immediately at ease in each other's company. There would be plenty of time for the roles to be reversed.

The next hour and a half flew past. Neither of them could quite work out how exactly, but it involved working their way all around his hotel suite. From the bed, he carried her to the stool she had so provocatively sat at earlier, according to him that is. There she leant back against the side as he withdrew his cock and devoured her with his tongue. 'So, so good,' she thought. Lou did love a bit of oral. Once he was back inside her, he plunged deep with his member, routing around to get in as far as possible, as Lou straddled the stool and his knees rubbed the thick carpet. Conscious of her back rubbing against the edge, he halted halfway through, ran into the bathroom and grabbed a towel for her comfort. What a star he was! It allowed him then to delve even deeper and with more force. Lou loved it.

From 'their' stool, they moved to the cream leather sofa. It felt cold on her back as he placed her upon it. Soon his cock returned to its rightful place, and they continued the pace, always looking deeply into each other's eyes. Wow, this was a super hot and horny session!

The bathroom was next, and why not? They were mid-tour, and this was adjacent to the lounge area. Against the double sinks was perfect for leaning over as he took her from behind. Slipping it in and out as they viewed their reflection in the mirror. Lou loved watching her own performance, and his gorgeous face and athletic body made for the perfect accompaniment. She put her right foot up on the sparkly black granite so she could see him sliding inside her. Warren delighted in this new angle and gripped her hips tighter. This was working for both of them; equally getting turned on even more.

"Ah fuck, I'm close," Warren said as he withdrew from her, with a slight look of panic on his face. "I don't want to come yet." Well, that was just as well, as Lou didn't want him to either. "I just need a minute. Let's go back to the bed." After some minor adjustment, they headed into the bedroom, bumping into each other on the way. It seemed that both sets of legs were a little weary!

Lou and Warren lay on the bed, snuggled up in each other. She fit perfectly under his left arm as she cuddled in close, with her hand caressing his chest. "Whoa," he said. "So fucking hot!" Lou couldn't agree more. "Just you tell me when it's safe to get on top. I've wanted to ride you all night." Warren smiled. "Oh really? Well now would be a good time." Lou followed his instruction and straddled his cock, ensuring the condom was still in place as she lowered herself down onto him.

Instantly he was rubbing against a pressure point inside her. With some light pushing down, Lou could feel she was about to gush. "Shall I get a towel?" She asked him. Warren knew what she meant. "Do you need to?" Lou jumped off and darted into the bathroom. "Probably wise," she said, returning swiftly and sliding the towel underneath him. She then assumed the former position. "Now, where was I?"

Grinding gently down, Lou found the spot once more. It felt good. She was just on the edge, and she could feel the pressure was getting to the point of no return. This would definitely be a gush and not a normal orgasm. It felt totally different. Having only just met Warren, she wasn't sure how he'd cope with her gushing, but in her experience, for some reason, men loved it. Feeling it run down their balls and onto the bed was usually a win-win situation. Let's hope he would feel the same way. 'Only one way to find out,' she thought as she let her body ride over the edge and unleash the fluid in plenitude. Her body gripped his cock as she let it out. Watching his face, she saw the delight and disbelief in his eyes. "Oh my god woman. There's loads of it. I can feel that all running down me." Lou smiled and nodded her head. Once more she found she couldn't talk at this point. It was too powerful. She would need a moment before normal functionality returned.

Still on top of him, Lou considered whether she should stay up there and now play with her clitoris. There was no point now being coy. She had just saturated him in her juices after all. Inhibitions were now destroyed. Licking her fingers, she placed them upon herself. Again, she spied the pure amazement in his eyes. Beginning slowly, she built up the momentum and force. Grinding at the same time, she got into her groove. This wasn't going to take her long. She was already a mass of mixed up nerve endings, waiting to burst once more, but the usual orgasm this time – the exploding fanfare type which would leave her body flinching throughout.

Lou could feel it building within her. "Yes Lou, come for me." Well, it would have been rude not to! Lou vigorously rubbed and there it was. She paused as the sensation consumed her. Clenching even harder onto his cock, her pelvic floor muscles went into spasm. Her whole body convulsed. There really was no better feeling than this. It was a big one and it was continuing for what felt like ages. "Fuck, fuck, I needed that!" Lou screamed as her body had let it all out. "Oh my god Lou, that was so horny to watch. You did need that." Lou started laughing. It was so true.

Continuing to force down into him, now slowly, he said, "I need to come Lou. Let me take this off and snuggle into me. I want you to watch me." Lou obliged. She was happy to lie under his arm once more. Having removed the condom, his right hand was now occupied massaging his cock forcefully. Lou placed her leg across him and began to rub her pussy on his side. "Oh yes Lou, grind into me. That's good. I bet you'd like someone to be fucking you from behind as you do that." Lou hadn't quite expected that, but she was happy to go with it. "Yes, I would like that. You'd feel me knocking against you as he fucked me." Warren was definitely getting off on this idea. "He could fuck you while I slept. I'd feel you getting fucked then he could shoot his load and then leave. I'd have to reclaim you as mine after." Lou liked the sound of that and purposely rubbed into him more energetically as if another man was taking her from behind. Her juices were covering Warren's left thigh as she rubbed. "Oh yes Warren, and he's so good too." Warren gasped. He was certainly enjoying it. "You're going to make me come," he whispered, and there it was, jets of sperm flew straight up and past Lou's left ear. There was some velocity! More spunk landed on Warren's groin and chest as he squeezed his penis tight and growled at the same time. "Oh

31

my god Lou," he sighed. "Fuck me. I needed that too!" That was obvious, given it was all over the place! Lou held him tight until his body recovered. She felt very comfortable there under his left arm, with her leg still wrapped around him.

After a while, Warren was ready to move again, and that was when they noticed the time. It was too late to go out and get some food now. After a quick clean up, room service was the order of the day. A bed picnic of burgers and chips felt like the best thing they had ever eaten. They appeared to have built up quite an appetite!

Once the food went down, they found themselves getting horny again, but this time they just kept it to the bedroom. There was no need to complete another circuit of the suite, maybe just another circuit of each other. It was almost 2am when they finally called it a day, only to wake up at 6am and have another round! Well, they were very compatible and who knew when they would be meeting again? Either way, they both knew the new day ahead of them would be a very long day in the office, and there would certainly be lots of yawning later, as well as some delicious memory flashbacks. They also knew it was well worth every last blast of energy they had exerted overnight and they would be doing it again sometime very soon.

Chapter 3 - Bet you think this story's about you

When Lou woke on a bright and sunny Monday morning, she had a deep desire to see Warren that evening. She was childfree and he was just the man to keep her company. Her message to him read, "I have a Warren-shaped itch that needs scratching. Can you help?" He replied immediately, "You'd best head to me tonight then." 'That's perfect,' Lou thought. It was exactly what she wanted to hear.

Their conversation continued as she headed into work and Warren's naughty imagination was soon sparked. "It would be awful if, on the way to me, you had an insatiable appetite for cock. You had to stop off on route and have someone else's dick before you met me. In fact, can you imagine how terrible it would be if I came back to my hotel and discovered you inside having sex with another person, right there in my room?" Warren added, "By the way, this would only work if it is with both our consents. Obviously I wouldn't know if this was going to happen or not. I'd have no knowledge if you're actually doing it or not when I was finishing work… but I'd allow it of course, and I just might find it incredibly horny x." Lou was immediately excited. This was thrilling and very, very different. She hadn't engaged in role-playing for some years, and this reminded her of just how exhilarating it could be.

"Would that not be disrespectful - to have sex with someone else in your room?" she asked. "Well no, not if I know it would turn you on, and it definitely would turn me on," Warren said. Lou thought this conversation was getting interesting indeed and from what Lou could gather, this was a resounding winning situation for her.

As was unusual but now becoming common practice, they both shared the same thought at the same time. "Now if I found you with another woman, that could be very interesting too." Damn! He beat her typing it before she did. It was an interesting proposal, and with a little more time, Lou was sure she could set something up. She would give it some thought. The worse case scenario would be Warren coming back to his hotel room and finding Lou draped in sexy lingerie, masturbating as he walked in.

A few messages were sent to two of Lou's bisexual female friends. She was sure that both of them would be keen to assist with her scenario. Unfortunately one of them was full of a head cold, and the last thing on her mind was travelling up to London to engage in some kinky action. Lou's second choice was grateful for the invitation, but it was too short notice, and she wouldn't be able to get a babysitter in time.

While setting a scene for Warren to find two women at play would be the ultimate discovery, this was proving a little difficult with just a few hours to go. Her next choice was to find a willing gentleman.

This should be an easier option, and there were a few she could call upon to enquire.

Her first choice was Marco, a top Sicilian barber living in London, who Lou had partied with on a few occasions. Lou met him a year ago at a fetish event, and they had fucked a number of times since. They had a good understanding between them, and that was pretty much that when they met up, they'd have sex together and they'd have sex with whomever else took their fancy too. They'd probably have sex together again afterwards as well. It was a partnership that worked!

David was the backup choice. Though Lou had never met him, he had been on her case to meet up for a very long time. He was going to be moving to Reading in the next few weeks and was keen to hook up before he went. Their conversations at the weekend had led to him offering to book a hotel for that evening (before she had chosen Warren for tonight). By booking David in for this adventure would kill two birds with one stone and also save him having to fork out for a hotel. This could be a potential if her first choice couldn't make it.

Lou messaged Marco with the message he admitted later that he had to share with some of his male friends. It wasn't the usual text he would receive, and he said his pals were stunned and in awe of him after he forwarded it to them. They asked him, "How do you know these people and who exactly gets that sort of message anyway?" It was indeed a different kind of world he lived in – the same crazy world as Lou.

Lou's speculative words were, "Marco, can I pinch you for a few hours this evening?" She was testing the water to see if he was free. He responded with, "Hello my darling. Tell me..." He was intrigued. Lou continued, "I need to be found in a hotel room fucking someone else. You'll be asked to leave afterwards." Marco was fascinated and stimulated at the same time. "He won't be violent, will he?" It was a fair concern and one Lou hadn't even considered. Although Lou had only met Warren twice, she very much doubted he would want to hit him. The most he was likely to do was to tell him to fuck off. If Lou's luck were in tonight, then maybe he would want Marco to stay and join in! Lou didn't know Warren well enough to decide which it was likely to be, but she remained hopeful.

Marco confirmed he would be able to join her and they sorted out logistics. The game was now afoot, and both of them were suddenly incredibly excited. For Lou, she found she was supercharged! She could think of nothing else. This was stimulation like she had never experienced before. Was this really happening? "OMG, OMG, OMG, OMG, game on!" was the message she sent to her close work friend Shantell and she knew exactly what she was referring to. Lou had met her for a coffee earlier in the day and explained the potential set up. Now this naughty scenario was about to be played out and Lou couldn't contain the exhilaration.

Lou messaged Warren and asked him what time he was likely to be back at the hotel. "Probably around 6pm at the earliest, I reckon." To feed his imagination and to begin the act, Lou said, "Well I would suggest you get back at around 6.30pm and if you are any earlier, then perhaps you'd like to go for a sauna?" Lou wanted him to know she was scheming and this would surely make him wonder what she was up to. "Oh, ok. I'll see what I can do and let you know nearer the time," he responded.

Lou left it there. She was feeling nervous, and she didn't want to give anything else away. She had planted the seed and knew it would be playing on Warren's mind now too.

Two work meetings under her belt later and Lou made her way to the Park Plaza Hotel. In her haste to get across, she discovered that she was a sweaty mess of hormones and desire. She desperately needed a shower and a 'de-fuzz' of the bodily hair, not that there was much, but she liked to have silky smooth legs and armpits. Her girly bits were recently waxed, so she was acceptable 'downstairs', as such!

Lou messaged Warren on the way. "Guess where I'm off to?" It was a little earlier than originally suggested, and it may have caught him a little off guard. "My heart's racing with excitement and anticipation. I have no idea what you are up to." "Mine is racing too," she answered but left it there. Lou wanted him to know something was brewing here.

Arriving briskly to the hotel, Lou went to reception where she was expecting the envelope containing the room key he'd left for her. However, this was not the case. They had nothing for her. Reception then pointed her to the concierge, who also couldn't find it. Lou was starting to get very flummoxed. For fuck sake, this was all she needed! She was already in panic mode and getting rather agitated, but she had to keep it together. Lou quoted his name and offered to show the guy on concierge the message Warren has sent her to prove it was authentic, but he said that was not necessary. He guided her back to reception, where two new keys were scanned and handed across to her. Thank goodness she could now head to the room and freshen up.

Lou was sure there was a conspiracy afoot. With three lifts to choose from, she was certain she would be in his room very swiftly. However, this was not the case. What seemed like an eternity passed before one arrived. Slowly it made its way up to the 13th floor where she finally got out. Outside room 1334, Lou swiped the card. The door light went from green to instantly red. In that split second, there was not enough time for Lou to grab the door handle to open it. She tried again, but this time there was no light at all. Armed now with key number two, Lou made another attempt but had the same outcome. What the fuck? She couldn't believe this was happening. How bloody difficult was it exactly to open a frigging door? Lou had no choice. She had to take the snail-like lift back to reception and get this sorted out.

It was a peculiar look she received from the receptionist, who had only just given Lou the cards. "Is everything ok?" Lou contained her desire to shout, "Well of course not otherwise I wouldn't bloody well be standing here, would I?" Instead, she was very polite and explained what had happened with the cards. "Perhaps my phone here has deactivated them?" Lou continued. The receptionist swiped them on her machine and said they should be working fine. Meanwhile, Lou was screaming inside her head, 'I just want to get in the poxy shower.'

Lou was assigned a security man, well more like a child who didn't look old enough to be working yet, to assist her upstairs. She had a chat with him in the lift, when it finally decided to show up and then she found herself outside the room again. As if to prove her inadequacy in performing a simple task, he tried the keys once more, amazingly (not) with the same results. "Well I don't know what's the matter here," he told her. Well, at least Lou knew she wasn't going mad. "I'll have to go back down to reception and call someone out." Lou was getting frantic. "Do you not have a master key you can let me in with?" Sadly, this was not the case. In her agitation, Lou told him she didn't have to come downstairs again and decided to wait outside the room.

Was this a test? Had Warren set this up as some sort of trial to see how she reacted? Was he watching her from somewhere and assessing her behaviour? This was starting to feel like some Saturday night prime time viewing of events that are set up to go wrong! Or maybe Lou reading just a little too far into this?

The longest eight minutes of her life passed as she waited for someone else to come and help her. When the engineer arrived, he tested again and told her that the battery in the card reader was almost flat and would need replacing. 'Why now of all times, for goodness sake? Hey ho. Let's try to stay calm,' she thought to herself. He let her in but warned he would have to come in with her to sort the battery out. Lou was relieved to finally be inside the suite and she messaged Marco to find out where he was. "Fifteen minutes away darling," he responded.

As the engineer left, Lou swiftly jumped in the shower and took care of her self-maintenance. Phew! She washed away the sweat (and foliage) and felt instantly better. Lou was now back in control. She dressed in her black shimmer basque, killer heels and recently reapplied mascara. Lou had time to take a picture of her shoed foot placed on 'their' stool from their last encounter and sent it across to Warren. She wanted him to know she was inside his hotel room, as this would add to his anticipation. Next was a selfie of her at the large dressing table, where she pretended to blow dry her hair. It was a great shot with her arms up, accentuating her muscly form, but also squeezing her cleavage together. This outfit was certainly a flatterer! Warren's response was quite simple: "Tease!"

Lou had brought a number of condoms with her. She placed them in the lounge area, the bathroom and the bedroom, as she had no idea where the fun would take place. There was always the possibility too that when Warren came in, he may just want to take her there and then, wherever that may be. Always best to be prepared and pretty much wherever it turned out to be, protection would be at the ready!

A further message to Marco giving instructions to the room was sent, but he was already outside a moment later, knocking on her door. It seems the lifts had not conspired against him. Lou checked the spy hole. He was standing there with a carrier bag. She could just make out the bottle of chilled Prosecco it contained.

Lou opened the door quickly and ushered Marco in and closed the door behind him. They were like a couple of excited school children - all giggly and silly. They had a hug and a kiss and then spoke about the crazy scene they were about to set up and play out. "You do know him, don't you? I mean, you have actually met him before?" Marco wanted to understand how well Lou knew him and she reassured him that he was a top guy, who she'd slept with the week before. He was kind, gorgeous and very unlikely to hit him! Marco was instantly relaxed, and she urged him to open the drink, which he soon did. They soon had a glass in their hands and were able to cope better with their planning.

They moved into the bedroom area. Marco sat down on the chair by the desk, and Lou stood next to him, describing how she had met Warren and the naughty fun they had experienced twice the week before. The alcohol was going down smoothly, and before they knew it, Marco's trousers were off and Lou's tongue was soon on his cock. He described how he'd already had fun earlier that day and he hoped he could still muster up enough energy to please her. "Oh it looks like it won't take much Marco," Lou said as his erection grew in her mouth. His breathing changed as she devoured him. "Oh

41

my god Lou, that's it. Yes, that's it. Come on, let's move to the bed."

For some reason, Lou's scruples kicked in when Marco suggested getting under the covers. She thought this was going a step too far and even though Warren and she had discussed this scenario being acceptable and not disrespectful, Lou couldn't help thinking this was somehow wrong. Maybe the sofa area would be better as they would both be sleeping in the bed tonight and she didn't want the inner sheets 'tarnished' as such. "But you have to make it look authentic," Marco said. Lou understood and agreed, but she was adamant they would not be getting up to mischief inside. "I'm sorry, I can't. That's just not on. Let's rough the quilt up a bit though so it looks like we were." Lou wasn't exactly sure why this made it more acceptable, but for some reason it did, and she was going along with it!

On the bed, Lou continued to give Marco oral pleasure. In between licks and strokes, they continued their conversation. "Thinking about it, where are all of your clothes? It's probably best that they are all in one place for when he comes in and kicks you out." It was a good point. Marco gathered all his bits to one side of the bed. Purposely they were not all in one tidy pile, as that would have looked contrived, but there were certainly all to hand.

Back to the bed and then it was Lou's turn to receive Marco; initially his tongue for a while and then he gave her his penis. The strategically placed condoms came in handy as the first one was

42

adorned and the pumping began. Knowing they could be walked in on at any moment added to the thrill. Marco was masterful as he fucked her, but Lou wanted to be on top – all the time wondering what the scene would look like should Warren walk in. Lou was literally riding on the wave of anticipation, and it was completely exhilarating!

It didn't appear that Marco was going to orgasm, so they decided to take a breather and Lou messaged Warren. "How long till you get here baby? I'm so bored waiting for you." It was quickly read, before she'd had time to take a good glug of her Prosecco. "Oh really? I thought you would have been amusing yourself. I'll be about twenty to thirty minutes." She didn't respond but instead left him hanging and stewing on the mystery that was playing out in his hotel room.

Back on the bed the two of them chatted about forthcoming parties and mutual friends. Lou liked Marco. He was easy-going, kind and a lot of fun to be with. They laughed about an encounter he had at a party they went to together recently, where he felt self-violated by sleeping with a very unattractive lady who pounced on him. As they were talking, Lou became conscious of the time and wondered how it would look if Warren walked in now. Marco was lying on the bed naked, Lou still in her basque and heels and two used, although not filled, condoms on the side. It would be obvious that sex had taken place here and likely that viewing this would still have the desired effect on Warren. However, to live up to the fantasy scenario he had expressed, it would be better still if she was being fucked as he walked in. Marco agreed.

They put their glasses to one side. The bottle was now empty anyway. He began teasing her with his tongue once more and made his way down to her clit. Whilst she was enjoying the attention it was getting, Lou was again thinking of the time. She turned over and told him to take her from behind. This excited Marco. "Of course, my lady," and he began doggy style.

Lou found herself lost in the moment and was moaning in delight. She was being vigorously pumped when Marco abruptly pulled out. What was going on? Why had he stopped fucking her? She looked behind her to the right at him. His face gave it away. "Oh shit! Sorry mate. I didn't know," he was saying. "She didn't tell me. Sorry." Lou thought, 'Holy shit – it was on!' Warren must have entered the room when she was in a far-away place being fucked silly. The adrenaline stepped up a notch to the point of intoxicating.

Lou looked to her left, still on her knees, and Warren was standing there, looking angered and in disbelief as he took off his coat to reveal his pristine suit beneath. She looked again at Marco, half smiling, but saw that he was playing his role perfectly. What a pro he was! He was picking up his pants, trousers and shirt as if to make a quick exit. Lou turned again to Warren. He was staring at her intently as he stood to the side of the bed. "Oh Warren, I'm so sorry, but I needed cock, and you were running late. I had no choice. I had to have him." He said nothing. He was still fuming. Marco said, "I should go. I'm so sorry."

Lou turned onto her back and lay down on the bed so she could see them both. She had half anticipated what happened next, but she could never be sure ahead of this exact moment. "No, you're alright mate." Warren told Marco, "You can stay for a while." This was music to Lou's ears. It was an ultimate and absolute success as far as she was concerned!

Warren removed his trousers and undid his shirt, then kneeled on the bed as Marco came back and did the same. Lou was now in the middle of them both. With two penises to amuse, she took it in turns to have them in her mouth. At the same time, they had their hands all over her body and inside her. Warren was fingering her rigorously, and she wondered if he was trying to make her gush. He had not done this to her before, whereas Marco had a few times on other occasions. "Marco, make me gush." It was a simple instruction, and he soon complied. Almost instantly the bed was saturated as he continued. It was the first time Warren had seen the effects with Lou, and he was visibly shocked. "Bloody hell Lou, you really can gush." Whereas Lou's practical head was on and she was thinking, 'so much for keeping the sheets clean eh?'

It was time now to focus on Warren. This was his fantasy after all that she had made happen for him (in record time too). His astonishment appeared to be subsiding, and she could feel he was relaxing more into the situation. Knowing how much he loved to be kissed, she grabbed his face with both hands and drew him to her. Her tongue forced its way inside his mouth, and they kissed passionately. It was time for him to be the centre of attention now.

Marco must have sensed the shift and soon said, "I think I'm going to leave you two to it." Jokingly, Lou said, "Yeah, fuck off Marco." The three of them instantly laughed. It was not meant to be insulting, and he took it in good spirits. "My work here is done," he retorted, and they thanked him as he got dressed and then said their goodbyes.

Warren took the opportunity to tidy up the room a bit as he let Marco out. Almost OCD-like, he wanted to remove traces of the other man. He disposed of the used condoms, wrappers and empty prosecco bottle. Now his head was clear, he returned to the bed to claim his woman back.

"Lou, you've been very naughty. Tell me it was only his cock you wanted. Tell me he meant nothing to you. You just needed cock before I got here. I was working too late, and you just couldn't wait, could you?" Back in the role, Lou responded, "I needed to be filled up, and you were going to be ages. My pussy needed some dick, and his was available. He's nothing. I just had to have someone warm me up for you Warren. Please don't think badly of me." Lou was impressed with her own skills here and was quite enjoying the reaction she created. "I know, and it's ok. But you know the consequences. I need to fuck him out of you now, don't I?" She stated, almost whimper-like, "Yes, Warren, please fuck him out of me and claim me back."

Warren's back arched as he became even more aroused. His cock felt instantly harder as grabbed a condom, put it on speedily and then rammed it inside her again and again and again. He was like a machine now, pummelling her forcefully. Lou was in her element, as Marco hadn't quite fulfilled her earlier. She gripped his back and locked her feet around him. Beads of sweat were forming on his forehead as he sank into her repeatedly. Lou screamed, "Fuck him out of me Warren!" And he certainly did. She could tell he absolutely loved it and oh boy, so did she.

Thinking this was the perfect end to the naughty role-play, she could tell he was close to coming. As swiftly as Marco had exited her earlier, Warren now withdrew with the same haste. "Not yet, not yet. I am SO close, but I don't want to come yet." 'Well this night really can't get any better,' Lou thought to herself. Not only had she made the scenario real for him; she had two men this evening, and this one wanted to carry on longer - perfect!

Warren slipped down the bed and began to lick her clit - all around it, all over it and from side to side. He was an oral king. His skills were remarkable, and they had her tingling every time his tongue went near her. "I can taste him on you," he said, "just like I could taste him on your tongue." Lou wasn't sure whether he approved or if she should take a shower. "It's ok. I like it. Shows me that you've had cock and now you are mine." 'Fair enough,' Lou thought. As long as he carried on with that masterful tongue of his, she didn't care.

CINNAMON TWIST

It wasn't long before she was grabbing the back of his head and pulling him into her pussy. Every nerve ending was on alert as he worked his magic down there. He was bloody good, and the build up was almost at a crescendo. More talented waves continued, and she exploded all over him. OMFG! At last! The mind-blowing orgasm she had been building to all evening was finally let out! It was enormous and went on for ages, with reverberations continuing for some time afterwards, made ever more tingly by Warren sticking his penis in her and pasting her more with it. All the adrenaline and excitement of today was now released, all over his face and his cock!

"I can feel your pussy gripping me." Lou couldn't respond. She could barely breathe let alone talk. The eruption was so strong, that her body was still in shock. And what a beautifully, fantastic shock it was too – exactly what she needed.

As Lou wriggled beneath him, he became aware that she wanted to be on top. "Oh, she wants to be in control eh?" Correct! He lay on the bed, and she straddled him. Making sure the condom was in place and not sucked off by her amazing pelvic floor muscles, she climbed on top. With all her strength, she ground down on him and rotated her hips. "Oh my god, I can feel every move you are making there. That's so deep," he said. He concentrated on his breathing to stop himself coming, as Lou sped up her motion. Deeper, faster, harder she dug into him. "Stop, stop! I don't want to come yet and you're going to make me." She eased off instantly. Again,

48

she was happy for him to hold off from coming just yet.

Lou leaned down and kissed his mouth, gently slipping her tongue in and rolling it around his lips, all the while with his penis still firmly inside her. As she moved across to the other side of his face, down to his neck, his soft stubble felt good on her cheek. She brushed past downwards and nibbled his neck, gently at first and then more enthusiastically. His body reacted instantly. "Oh my god Lou. That is so, so good."

Lou sat up now and slipped two fingers of her right hand into her mouth. They then made their way to her clit, and while she was riding him, she rubbed herself energetically. She could feel she was very close to coming again and told him so. "Oh, that's it. I'm really close..." Before she could finish, she was hit again by another massive orgasm. Her body tensed as she let it out. Meanwhile, Warren looked up in pain. "Shit! I'm not strangling you am I?" Lou had experienced this with other lovers in the past. Her pussy would grip so hard in orgasm that it felt like she was cutting off their circulation. "A little bit," Warren murmured. This was eased as the after shocks subsided. Lou sat on top of him for a while to calm down. Her pussy was tingling and her body flinching for some time before she could resume play.

Refreshed, Lou was ready once more. She slowly began to build up the momentum, but the earlier blood loss meant Warren would be hard again sooner if he were on top. Lou happily complied. He was beautiful to look up at after all.

CINNAMON TWIST

His dirty words started again. "You just needed cock, didn't you? Now I need to claim you back." Lou knew where this was going. "Yes, Warren. Now fuck him out of me!" Again the pounding began - harder and harder with each thrust. He was relentless. She wanted to sink her nails deep into his back but knew this was not allowed. Instead, she brushed them across his skin gently. He arched his back in delight, and his goose bumps had returned. That seemed to hit the spot.

"Ah Lou, I think I'm gonna come." "Then come Warren. Let it all out, all over my tits," she encouraged him. "Ah, ah, ohhhhh…" and there it was. Hastily he removed the condom and aimed his cock at her torso. She held his left arm as the spunk soon jetted past her right shoulder while other streams were deposited on her belly. None of it actually landed on her breasts, but he made a pretty pattern all the same! "Ahhhh," he continued as the last drops left his throbbing cock. His tense body was erect above her, and she continued to hold him as his shoulders then dropped, and he lay next to her on the bed.

Wow, what an intense session that had been. They stayed on the bed in the same position for a while, talking and laughing about the events of this evening. Warren got up and brought some tissues back from the bathroom. After sweeping up the mess he'd left, he quickly washed. Lou decided to hit the shower and once clean, came back to find Warren hair drying the bed! He was doing a good job too!

50

CINNAMON TWIST

You would have thought that after the intense fantasy that was played out this evening, the pair would have been spent. Instead, they were so turned on when they came to recall how they were feeling throughout the day, with the not knowing what was going on, the immense adrenaline build up and the pure excitement, that they didn't even get around to eating that night. Instead, more sex ensued, with more fantasies spoken about, ideas exchanged, and the pinkie promise of regular plaything status achieved. There were certainly more adventures on the cards for this naughty pair. 'Bring it on,' Lou thought, as she finally slipped off to sleep after an amazing, yet exhausting adventure with this delightful man.

Chapter 4 – Getting acquainted with Paul

It was Lou's first fetish party and promised to be full of glamour as well as naughtiness. Having finally met the rather delicious friend Cameron the week before, she was only too delighted to use his spare ticket and tag along. The understanding was that they would go together but were free to meet and play with whomever they fancied - literally.

The evening was eventful and lots of fun. There was a latex catwalk display that was interesting and then some rather quirky scene acted out with fake blood being poured over a few women. Lou couldn't quite understand what that was all about, but others seemed to enjoy it. Following that the excellent club music took over and Lou and Cameron danced way into the early hours.

Lou met an attractive Sicilian and enjoyed the mutual pleasure they enjoyed, both on the dance floor in front of everyone and then upstairs in one of the open rooms. He was certainly hot; black hair he flicked to one side, fit body, not so well endowed, but the thrill of being the centre of attention made up for that.

A number of the hot partygoers were going onto an after-party and both Cameron and Lou were keen to join them. At 3am, it seemed too early to be concluding this rather decadent evening and so on they went.

They found themselves now in North London at a flat a number of them shared. Some fixed decks were in place and the music was already blaring. To Lou's surprise, a fixed pole was also in use, with a number of would-be pole dancers having a go. Lou was transfixed for a while but was soon distracted by the entertaining conversation one of Cameron's old friends had sparked up with them. Paul was ripping the shit out of his mate and he had Lou in stitches. He was hilarious. Lou liked him instantly. Cameron gave it back in equal measure and was a great sport.

Paul was here with his girlfriend Lisa, but she was nowhere to be seen. She was probably in the other room on the sofas, where a group of them were passing joints around as more were being rolled up. Lou didn't get to meet her, but Paul did sing of her praises. Lou found herself easily getting involved with Paul's banter, and they did have a good laugh at Cameron's expense.

The after-party continued into the morning and the threesome found themselves outside continuing their tête-à-tête in the May sunshine. It was glorious to have the sun beating down on them, but Cameron and Lou were growing tired. Unlike many others, they were fuelled only on alcohol, and it was time now to get back to the comforts of his house. This did not mean the fun stopped, in fact, another rather beautiful and dominant female accompanied them both for an afternoon and evening of pleasure.

All in all, it was a very good introduction to a different kind of night, with some new people Lou knew she would have the opportunity to have more amusement with in the future, although she never expected one of those would be Paul.

He found Lou on Facebook soon after the party and then added her on Instagram. Over the summer they would like each other's updates and throw in the odd comment here and there, but that was about it. So Lou was quite surprised to hear from him directly in October, just as she had decided to sell her ticket to an event that night. His message began, "Hey gorgeous. Will I have the pleasure of seeing you tonight?" 'Damn,' Lou thought. He must be going along too. So many of her acquaintances were all going to the same event, but she didn't realise he would be, nor was she expecting such flirting. "I was really hoping to see a lot more of you, Lou." Well, that was a surprise.

It transpired that Paul and Lisa had split up over the summer and now he was on the prowl. He'd apparently fancied Lou since that first party, but the timing and the circumstances were all wrong for him. Now he was a free agent and trying his luck. Lou was disappointed that she had decided not to go out, but she had a feeling their time would come.

Another month or so passed as their diaries failed to align, but finally, they met up for some drinks and dinner. They planned to meet at Waterloo underground station where they would grab a quick drink there before deciding where to head to next. Given it had been over six months since they had last seen each other, Lou did wonder if there would be any physical attraction. She knew Paul entertained her mind and had a very quick wit, but would the animalistic instinct take over?

When they met, Lou felt it was a little awkward to start. Their conversations were all rather formal, as to be fair, they didn't really know each other. Fortunately, both were great communicators and it wasn't long before they both lightened up and relaxed. A gin and tonic for her and a beer for him probably helped as they chatted on in The Wellington pub.

They decided to make their way back to his house. It was a short train ride away and by this time they wanted to explore the unfamiliar and rather enticing territory of each other before them.

At Paul's, they bumped into his flatmate and made their introductions. He soon retired to his bedroom and left them to their devices upstairs. Paul poured some prosecco and they both made themselves comfortable on his sofa. As he edged closer to her, she noticed how much weight he had lost since she first met him. He said he had dropped over a stone in weight and had never felt better. Now Paul was slight already, and Lou didn't really feel he would have needed to lose any weight. His frame was sleek and he was tall, standing around 6′ 2″ with strawberry blond hair. His green eyes were sparkling in anticipation. There was certainly something about him that was very attractive.

Without any prompt or suggestive talking, Paul turned to her and caressed her face. "I've wanted to do this for a very long time," he said as he slid his tongue in her mouth. 'Mmm,' she thought as she met his tongue with hers. Well that was a much better kiss than she had expected. For some reason Lou thought he would be slobbery, but no, not at all. He reached across and lowered her down to lying on the sofa.

What followed next was intense; like they had saved it up all night until this moment, when hands were suddenly flying everywhere, groping, grabbing and feeling. Clothes were doing the same as they were pulled over their heads, down over hips and before they knew it, they were both naked and skin on skin. The passion was extreme. and Lou loved it!

After more kissing, Lou made her way down to see what he'd been , packing, and she wasn't disappointed. His cock was of a decent size at around seven to eight inches, but it was more pencil-shaped, as in quite narrow. It would definitely hit the spot, as she was soon to find out, but that was not her usual process. Lou always liked to spend time providing oral pleasure to her partners, and she had a feeling he would savour every stroke and lick of her tongue, which he certainly did.

Paul's face was a picture as she worked her magic and he began to sigh as she took the full length of his penis in her mouth. Lou tried her utmost not to gag on it as she deep-throated him, but she could feel her eyes begin to fill and her mascara become in danger of running. He put his hand on the back of her head very gently and held it softly as she drew herself up and down upon it. He threw his head back at the same time, taking in the full pleasure.

The thicker saliva produced upon this gagging reflex was now coating his cock, and she slid her hand up and down it intentionally softly. His face now displayed pure bliss. Lou continued to caress it delicately with her hand and could see how much he was enjoying it. "Fuck Lou. That feels so good. Wow, yeah, keep doing that!" It was obviously having the desired effect, so Lou was a little surprised when he asked her to put a finger up his anus. It had been a while since Lou had done this with anyone, but she knew how the bum is so very sensitive, so it wasn't exactly a shock. She just didn't expect this on their first date! This was normally something that would be requested or offered after a few sexy encounters with the same partner. But Lou was no prude. She licked her index finger and slowly entered him. It slipped in very easily and his glee was more evident now with the increased sighing and moans.

If Paul wanted her fingers up his arse, Lou would not disappoint. And 'fingers' was the appropriate word here because the next thing he said was "stick another one in Lou." Again, she obliged, having spat on her fingers this time to aid entry. Slowly inside and then back out again, finger-fucking his bottom. "Another one Lou," and now three were inside him. She raised it to four without his request and continued the in-out motion. He was seriously getting off on it, but Lou wanted some attention now.

Being a little OCD about hygiene, she made a quick dash to the sink and washed her hands; then she made her way back to the sofa where he was waiting. ('Another thing they never show in porn movies,' she thought and smiled to herself.) She reconnected with his cock and took it deep in her mouth. After some minutes, she made her way back up to his face. She wanted him to taste himself on her as she kissed him deeply. Paul loved this exchange and wanted more, but Lou had other intentions. She was horny as hell and wanted to be devoured.

Lou positioned herself next to him and lied on her back. He knew exactly what was next. Whipping himself up and above her, Paul was suddenly between her legs and lapping her up with a real thirst. It was her time now to lay back and relish her moment.

Paul's oral skills would not be up there in her top three, but they were ok. With a little assistance, she would soon achieve that orgasm she was seeking. Bringing her right hand down to where he was focussing, she began to rub her clit. Paul continued to lick her, but his tongue was clashing with her fingers. Instead, she guided him lower, so he was dipping his tongue inside her. "Your turn to put your fingers in me, Paul." Perfect! Now she would definitely come. In and out with his fingers in her vagina while rubbing herself soon built up enough momentum and arousal to tip her over the edge. There was the crescendo she sought and the explosion. "Thank fuck for that!" Lou shouted. It just came from nowhere, and she rode the waves as they washed over her. God, she needed that!

Now it was time to have his cock inside her. He pulled out a condom from the drawer in his coffee table and put it on. Lou wanted to ride him, but he had other ideas. Having had her fingers inside him and watched her come, Paul wanted to fuck her hard. Missionary position it was for most of their session, but it wasn't boring. He had her in all different angles and leg raised combinations, all in the effort to get in as far as possible. It certainly worked. He had her gushing all over his sofa, and this then turned him on even more.

"Will it turn you on if I come all over your tits?" Lou didn't really care where he put it, to be honest. It had been a powerful entangling and he had worked hard for his own orgasm. "Yes, you go for it." It took no time at all for Paul to whip his cock out from her, pull the condom off and shoot his hot spunk all over her. Some of it did actually reach her breasts, but most of it landed on her stomach. This gave them both a reason to laugh once he'd finished shaking. "I'm gonna really have to work on my aim!" Paul mused.

It was getting late, but Paul suddenly opened up to Lou in a way she had never expected. It seemed he had a whole different world he wanted to share, and Lou was the prime focus of it. Lou had no idea. Paul wanted to explore many fantasies around the dominant and submissive world, and he wanted Lou to be heavily involved in this – in fact, to be the sole focus of it all. This would take some more thorough discussion, but in principle, this was looking like a mutually beneficial collaboration that Lou was very eager to commence with. They planned to meet again and discuss the terms of engagement before any arrangement began.

Chapter 5 – Ben Travis

Well, that was a first. Never had Lou's armpits been licked in the middle of a steamy sex session before. Her initial response was shock and disbelief, but when you've been massaging a wand into a man's arse while wanking him off at the same time, it seems a little contradictory to think that some harmless armpit licking action is off the menu. It's hardly time to get squeamish when he's just gulped down your gush as he continuously triggered it.

It was their third meeting and once again Lou found herself physically exhausted at the end, to the point where she could barely string a sentence together as they reflected on four hours of full-on sex. It had been quite a night!

Ben was not her usual type in that his body was not the lean, cut, toned Adonis she was partial to. It was fair to say he was sporting a little bit of a potbelly, which was forgivable considering his intense bedroom skills. His body was covered all over in 'salt and pepper' coloured hair, and we are talking unkempt, natural, full-length hair everywhere. The only exception was a carefully carved out triangle that provided easy access to his lovely cock, that Lou had the pleasure of worshipping a few times now. The hair on his head and chin was also thick, long and beautifully coiffured.

Ben's best feature and the one that took her breath away were his eyes. OMG how Lou melted into them; bright blue, piercing and sparkling, they looked up at her with intent and menace as Ben had devoured her pussy on that first occasion. Her juices saturated his beard as she came and came again for him. God, he was good. He made her explode without putting anything inside her, and that was a first. He used his tongue with skill, paying attention to her clit, labia and vagina walls. By using just his thumbs, Ben massaged the sides and opening. Lou had so desperately wanted to cry out and tell him to shove a finger or two in, but she resisted. She would go with this and see where it led. It wasn't like she wasn't enjoying it, just petering on the edge of orgasm. Just wanting that little extra nudge over. So, so very close and then finally "HOLY SHIT! OH FUCK! YES!" (Sometimes Lou couldn't quite work out where these outbursts came from, but it was the right thing to shout out at that particular moment.) The gargantuan orgasm erupted inside her and consumed her body. With her arms already raised above her head, Lou gripped the pillows tight and let the waves of pure bliss ride through her. Oh wow – this was amazing! And yet still Ben continued licking until she could take no more. Hard as she tried, she had to push him off in the end, as it was all proving too tingly to take.

Once recovered, Lou demanded to ride Ben and naturally he did not object. He'd enjoyed her hips grinding down into him before and the continuous flow of juices running down either side of his penis, saturating his balls and the bed beneath them. Lou was very fortunate to be able to do this pretty much on demand if the angle was right and she was turned on enough. Again and again, Lou drenched him underneath her, much to his delight. She couldn't help but feel for the poor hotel cleaners who would have to deal with this bed in the morning!

Lou's gushing abilities did baffle her somewhat, and she often wondered where it all came from. She was told that it was due to over-exciting a particular gland up inside her, but how on earth did she get that wet? Years ago she had thought she was urinating while gushing, but many a time (post-intercourse) Lou had emptied her full bladder in the loo or shower, depending on whom she was sharing the shower with! There was no way 'gush' could be urine, well not in Lou's mind. Surely there would be no wee after sex if it were? It was a mystery.

It didn't take Lou long to come again as she rode Ben and thought less and less about the wrecked furniture. This position really worked for her, and she was able to force herself down so he could feel every part of her engulfing him, as she spied his amazing eyes sparkle even more contentedly.

Whilst the gushing and coming were a-plenty, Lou was seeking the mind-blowing crescendo-type orgasm once more. She chose to handle this one in her own special way – which was always welcomed with much excitement from her partners.

Lou licked the fingers of her right hand (not that she needed any additional lubrication down there) and began to rub her clitoris. Lou knew her body well enough to know this wouldn't be a drawn-out process. "Ah… this won't take long," she told Ben as she furiously continued and she was correct. "Oh god yes; almost there." Lou almost whispered the words. Ben was dumbstruck below her and positively encouraging her to continue her frantic massaging with his stare and nodding. "Yeah, yeah, yeah; here we go!" Lou said, and there it was. It was deep, and it was a lingerer – just what Lou loved. The long, drawn out orgasms were to die for. Lou revelled in the reverberations as they swept through her being. "Hell yes!" she continued as her insides gripped Ben's cock ever tighter. His face looked perplexed beneath her, wondering how her body was tightening around him, but he was savouring every moment and twitch.

On the other occasions they had played, Lou had found herself riding Ben for quite a long period and exploring a multitude of positions before his inner animal was freed. Each time Lou was surprised with the volume and depth of his explosion. He really did assume a wolf-like howl, to decibels unheard of before. With a body covered in that much hair, Lou wondered how she would fare if it were a full moon?

Tonight was different. Ben had brought his bag of goodies along with him to the hotel. Lou's first introduction to 'the bag' had been when he produced it in a swinging club recently. Lou was devouring his cock when he reached to the side of the sofa and grabbed it. She hadn't even realised it was there. From within, he produced an instrument for the tip of his penis. It was thin and long, with a small handle on the end. Lou was to discover he called it his sounding rod and she watched in awe as it was forced all the way down the length of his 'japs eye'. It began slowly to start, and he had used his own saliva as lubrication, which may not have been ideal. Lou could feel it under the skin as she devoured him in front of a number of others, purposefully licking where it was protruding. Ben appeared to be enjoying it, however, when it came to retracting the tool, Lou could see some blood on the end. "Proper lube next time," he said, but he still seemed to have adored the experience, possibly because he was the centre of attention, as well as the sensation this had delivered physically. Even the club owner had enjoyed watching Lou's mouth in action as he had wandered past earlier and stopped in his tracks to stare. He even joked about him being next, knowing full well that his girlfriend would probably have cut his balls off if she saw him in action with a patron.

From the bag this time Lou was surprised to find Ben withdrawing a wand sex toy. It was identical to the one Snake Hips had treated her to the year before on one of his visits. "Oh, that's funny. We have the same one," she delighted in telling him - only this time it wasn't for her.

Ben was the first bisexual man Lou had slept with. Actually that may not have been necessarily true. Ben was the first man who openly admitted being bisexual who Lou had slept with. As one of Lou's remaining fantasies was to have an all bi-MMF (male, male, female), he was certainly looking like becoming a promising candidate to fulfil this one with her.

Lou had heard of many men in couples on sex sites who claimed to be straight, but this may not have necessarily been the case. When single men came to join them for threesomes with their wife or girlfriend, the single males often found themselves in compromising positions with the male part of the couple. Some married men or boyfriends wanted the extra man there for their own pleasure as much as for their woman, and this set up was all just a front. Lou had spoken to a few single males and found them recalling stories of getting into arguments when they declared they were not gay. When it came to 'crossing swords' and their penises touching, in a double vaginal penetration, for instance, single men could often find they were getting more than they had bargained for.

But Ben was openly bisexual and this was all very new and interesting to Lou. Obviously his sphincter was a centre of arousal and one she would focus on more so given his preferences. It seemed the most natural thing in the world then to lube the wand up and have it rubbing around his sensitive bottom. She put the condom on his toy as requested and began to rim him with it in circular motions. Ben's breathing grew heavier, and he sighed as she built up the momentum.

Next Lou moved down to the area in between his balls and anus. Bigger circles were drawn and she pushed the wand into him as she continued. She could tell he was enjoying it as she felt him wriggle beneath her touch and some gasps escaped him. 'Well this is different,' Lou thought, 'great too though,' as he grew closer to orgasm.

"I need to be inside you, Lou." She was not going to argue with that. She wanted him in there as much as he wanted to be, plus her right arm was getting achy with all this pushing around and around and into him with the wand. Lou felt positively relieved to put it down. It was her turn for some attention again. Oh goodie!

Ben grabbed a fresh condom and put it on. "Bend over here and let me fuck you." Lou complied and went down on to all fours on top of the bed. This allowed him easy access to assume the doggy style position. "You know I'll come quicker like this though?" Of course, she did. A good number of men Lou had slept with would ejaculate faster in this style than any other. It was always the one she chose when she was tired (or bored, which was not the case here)! "I have no objections," she stated clearly.

The growls commenced from behind her. Lou licked her fingers once more and caressed her clit, but she knew it would not be leading to anything further. It was more for show. Men so loved watching a woman pleasuring herself, from any viewpoint and she could sense it was turning him on. As he plunged himself inside her with continued force, she pushed herself back on him to get even deeper and feel the full effect. It was working for them both, although Lou knew she wasn't going to come again, neither did she need to. She didn't want to any more this evening as she had already had her fill of explosions and gushing for one night.

Louder growls followed as the volume switch steadily went up a few notches. Moments later and there it was. Ben had reached the point of no return. It was quite possibly the loudest orgasm she had ever heard in a man, just narrowly overtaking Pearls of Wisdom in its length and depth, and this time in this meagre hotel room, it didn't matter if their neighbours heard.

Lou grabbed the backs of his thighs and pulled him in tight as he shot his load inside her. Gripping him there in place, she waited until he had stopped quivering. It was a strong union, and both of them felt they had worked hard for this finale. They would hold this position for a while yet.

As normal breathing resumed, Lou asked, "Is the condom ok?" It was an issue she had experienced with Ben repeatedly. She kept gripping the condom off his cock with her vagina, and it didn't seem to matter what position they were in, Ben would have to go in manually to retrieve it. Maybe those pelvic floor exercises did work after all! Lou had kept them up after all her children were born but soon became bored with that type of clenching. This type was far more fun. Or maybe it was because, as she'd recently learned, your pelvic floor muscles grow during pregnancy. Either way while Ben wasn't the first man to have to search for the missing condom; he seemed to be the most frequent! Fortunately, they were all intact, even the full ones, as was the case now!

These were the events that led to Lou and Ben finding themselves in a restaurant with so very little to say. They were famished after their session and needed some nourishment. The food gave them another round of energy, but what they both needed was sleep and rejuvenation. Such was their exhaustion that they could either eat or talk. Doing both was proving nigh on impossible, not that anyone was complaining. Instead, they revelled at their achievements!

Following this evening, when Lou thought about the condom situation, she decided it would be useful to seek advice and get some different opinions. It was suggested that the condoms might not have fit properly, but they certainly looked snug when adorned. Or was there too much moisture inside them and therefore they did not grip the penis tightly? Was Ben unnecessarily generous in thinking he needed the larger condom, when in fact the standard size would suffice? Lou had no idea, but she was getting concerned that this was not proving a particularly safe sex practice and would have to be addressed.

Lou decided, after a few days and then weeks passed, that perhaps this would not have to be dealt with after all. There were a few of Ben's actions that made her feel increasingly uneasy. They were not derogatory in any shape or form, but she did question if he was becoming emotionally attached to her. She may have been over-thinking it, but her gut feeling was usually right. Considering he was married, it did feel that he was becoming a little bit obsessed and that was like a red rag to Lou. It was the same old scenario that she had experienced before with previous sexual partners. She would befriend a good man, give him something he absolutely adored (usually escapism from his normality) and suddenly Lou was the centre of his world. Well, that was how Lou interpreted it anyway. They would probably tell the story very differently, but that's what instinct told her.

While they had shared some kinky naughtiness together of a very high standard, Lou thought it was probably safer all round if she politely removed herself from frequent interactions with him. She didn't want him to reach an even deeper level with her, as this would be more difficult to reverse when she inevitably called it a day. It was the better option for Lou. He was fun, and the sex was exceptional, but he didn't qualify to be taking up all of her spare time when away from her Mum duties, and this was where it seemed to be heading. By calming things down now, it allowed them to continue having a flirty friendship without any drama. No doubts there would be more hot and steamy sex between this pairing, but not at every spare moment she had. Lou didn't like those kinds of limitations.

One of the triggers for this chain of thought was when Lou mentioned she had plans to go to a private sex party at a swanky West End hotel in London. It was a mid-week event that Lou had been to a couple of times before. The quality of guests was always high as the organisers carefully chose who was invited. This meant supplying a photo of any new wannabe guests for approval, which guaranteed the standard and the reputation of the parties. Lou always provided a photo of her potential 'plus one' and this evening was no exception. She messaged them in advance and informed them she was bringing a rather delectable Italian called Lui, whom she met in December at a fetish night. They soon sent a confirmation email through, and they were good to go!

These particular parties were usually intimate affairs, with ten couples, five single males and five single females. The numbers worked. It was just the right size for the two-bedroom penthouse suite with stunning views over the Houses of Parliament and Big Ben. They were always very active, and that's probably why Lou enjoyed them so much.

Lou told Ben she had plans to go along to the party when he'd asked what she was up to that week. With it being her childfree week, he knew she would have things arranged. (Her diary did tend to fill up quickly with socialising, exercise classes and meets.) He immediately went on to say that he would contact the organisers, so she assumed he had been to their events himself before. What Lou had not anticipated was Ben telling them he would be accompanying Lou as her guest! This did not bode well with Lou as she had never asked him nor implied for him to go as her partner. This put both the organisers and Lou in a tricky position. As all the single male spaces were filled, they suggested she chose whom she was coming along with, but Lou had already made that decision before. Lou would have to man up and confront Ben with it.

Both Lou and Ben were adult enough with broad shoulders. She was sure he would be fine once the situation was explained fully. Fortunately, it was easier to tackle. Lou managed to amicably resolve the situation by providing a female friend who agreed to partner up so he could get in as a couple. It was an unnecessary situation that could have been avoided if he hadn't been so presumptuous and it did get Lou's back up somewhat.

On another occasion, Lou was equally taken aback after booking a week's holiday to her favourite island and mentioning it to Ben in passing. Much to her astonishment, he took this as a green light to jump into action. She had no idea he would take steps to accompany her there too. A week or so later he said he shocked Lou by telling her he had cleared it with his wife! 'What the fuck?' Lou wondered. What on earth was he thinking? Lou had given no impression whatsoever that she wanted company on this trip.

Pangs of fear were sent running through Lou's mind. She had to nip this in the bud right there and then. "You know when I go to Gran Canaria I go solo, right?" It was awkward to mention, but the last thing Lou wanted was a cock-block there of all places. It was the place she felt most liberated, and she certainly didn't want to feel in any way restricted. To his credit, Ben did see the error of his ways and politely withdrew his offer to join her. "Oh, I'm sorry. Did I just go and invite myself on holiday with you?" Lou confirmed but didn't budge on her feelings. She was sure he thought she'd say to come along, even for part of her time there, but that wasn't what Lou wanted, so she left it there.

Similar to when she was in Gran Canaria, when back in the UK Lou liked the freedom to come and

71

go as she pleased and with whomever she pleased. By spending too much time with Ben, it was beginning to worry her somewhat. He may have seen her as his new party partner, but Lou didn't want to give him too many ideas or false hopes. She had to manage his expectations, and in her mind she knew it was time to wean him off.

It was a shame. There had been so many fantasy ideas too, so Lou was a little disappointed to have come to this decision, but she felt it was the right thing to do. It had happened time and time again. As soon as Lou felt in the slightest bit trapped or heading in that direction, it was time to move on. She wasn't ready to bring anyone in close enough to see the real her or to have the real her – well not all of her. She didn't feel anyone was quite worthy of that just yet. She was having too much fun in this lifestyle to change it. Maybe one day she'd be ready, but she'd tried it before and knew the timing still wasn't right, if it would ever be so?

Ben and Lou remained in contact and became very good friends. She had a funny feeling their sexual paths would cross again, particularly as they frequented the same locations, knew many of the same people and chatted quite a lot. She also thought he might orchestrate such a 'coincidence', which wouldn't have been a problem, even if Lou didn't still believe in coincidences.

Chapter 6 – Wanton Warren

Lou and Warren were now firmly established fuck buddies. They had pinkie promised to be, after all. Whenever he was in town, they managed to find a way to ensure their paths, and most definitely their intimate parts, crossed. In fact, Lou couldn't get enough of him, which was unusual. She didn't normally tend to be all absorbed like this. Maybe it was because she couldn't have him whenever she wanted him. Lou had to wait for him to be in London and their diaries aligned.

Warren had certainly awakened her naughty side in a way not seen for some years. He enjoyed pushing different boundaries and liked to see how far Lou would go with his delicious scenarios. This was facilitated by Lou, who was also thinking of similar situations they could explore together.

It was a Wednesday evening and Warren had clients to entertain after work. Lou also happened to be free and they arranged to meet at 9pm. Before that Lou thought she would use the time wisely. She met a gorgeous looking couple in a bar in Canary Wharf. They arranged to have a drink and check each other out to establish whether there would be any potential playing at another time. He was a policeman and she worked in finance.

When Lou entered the bar, she found him

waiting for her at a large table. She could see he had finished a coffee. He was on duty later so wouldn't be having any alcohol. The conversation immediately flowed and his company was very easy, as was he on the eye. He was in his early thirties, with a fit body and was sat there with a smile on his cute face, as he told Lou what he and his girlfriend were looking for. Lou knew from the moment she sat down (and possibly before) that she would definitely have some naughty time with this young hunk. She hoped his girlfriend was of the same quality.

Some fifteen minutes later she appeared. At around five feet and two inches, she was blonde, petite and beautiful. They did make a lovely couple and they certainly bounced off each other with mischievous banter as soon as she joined them. There were smiles all around. This was a grouping that definitely would work.

The 'quick drink' that was supposed to last for up to an hour lasted nearly two, so that was a good sign. They exchanged stories of previous encounters and the couple explained that they were relatively new to the 'scene'. Even with their short exposure, they had some funny anecdotes about parties they had attended and the different people they had met. Effortlessly they continued to the point where Lou said, "I'm sorry, but I need to be somewhere else." She told them of her plans, and while departing, they agreed to meet in the next few weeks, possibly at a club or party, where they were all looking forward to getting naked together.

Lou's next stop was dinner with a guy she'd met

at a party some five months before. She had attended it with her kilted friend and this was a pal of his. Out of the blue, Paul messaged Lou the weekend before, and their conversation took an unexpectedly saucy direction. He had split with his girlfriend and wondered if Lou was out on Saturday night? It transpired that Lou had originally been going to the same fetish event, but had changed her mind and sold the ticket from her bath that evening. Instead, dinner was arranged for tonight, before she went off to see Warren for 'dessert'.

Just as Lou was freshening up to head towards the Underground, Paul messaged. Sadly he was still tied up with work, and he wouldn't be able to get to her until 8pm. Would it be possible to postpone? A little disappointed, Lou agreed and was glad she had packed her gym kit that morning. Even though she had a gin and tonic inside her, she would still get a work out in, and that's exactly what she did.

While Lou was having a post-cardio stretch, her phone rang. It was her rugby friend affectionately known as Pants. What a surprise. She'd seen him at a party a few weeks before but they hadn't had sex for months. "Hello, gorgeous. And what is one up to this evening?" Lou explained she was in the gym and had someone to meet later. "Well me and a few of the lads are in Soho. Why don't you come down?" Well, that was tempting, especially as she had a bit of a soft spot for one of those other lovely lads. It was the same one who had just so happened to tell her on the phone not to wash but to come straight to them in her gym kit! On this chilly autumn evening, she would do no such thing, especially as she had a beautifully fitted dress for Warren later. Here she would get the chance to display it to her rugby friends as well, which Lou saw as a complete bonus!

Freshly showered Lou embarked on her journey. It was cutting it a bit fine to get across town and be on time for Warren, so she messaged him asking if 10pm was too late to arrive. It suited him better as he was still having dinner. Perfect! Off the tube at Leicester Square, Lou found the restaurant they were plotted up in, or so she thought. They were nowhere to be seen. It seemed there were two restaurants with the same name not too far apart. Whilst walking around the square, Lou heard a distinct snap as her left heel broke underneath her. "Oh for fuck's sake!" she shouted out, not caring who heard.

She tottered to Charing Cross Road and hailed a black taxi. The journey took less than ten minutes and she was glad not to be putting any weight on her damaged shoe. She was carrying her gym bag, so at the very worst her trainers would be coming out, but not yet, not with this lovely dress on.

It was great to see the three of her rugby friends at the restaurant, and a gin and tonic was ordered on her behalf as soon as she sat down. Kisses all round and then a generous serving of their combined Italian dishes was presented to her. She hadn't expected to be joining them for dinner, but since the exercise earlier, Lou was ravenous. You could always count on the rugby chaps to be true gentlemen with their manners. They could fiercely take the piss and have her rolling around in laughter, but they would always have her back too, bless them – such was the mutual appreciation and fondness.

Another drink later and she knew she'd have trouble moving on. They were funny and flattering, which was just what Lou loved. They were cheeky too, but tonight's conversations were also quite deep, and it showed Lou another side of the third man dining. Lou gained some respect for him and was pleased she'd come out, even if she had been attempting not to hobble when she rocked up to meet them.

Lou messaged Warren to say she'd be another forty minutes or so and was surprised when he said her dinner dates could come back too. For a few moments she contemplated this, and they certainly seemed keen when she advised them, but logistically Lou thought it might prove problematic. They were steaming into the red wine and were having a bit of a heart to heart too. Not only that, but she thought Warren wouldn't know what had hit him if they did all bundle back. Three stocky ex-rugby players, all over six foot, taking it in turns might be a little bit tricky. It was also a school night, and she rarely had much sleep when she was with Warren anyway. This would mean zero sleep and although it would be a lot of fun, Lou decided against it. Warren was rarely in town, and tonight she selfishly wanted him all to herself.

Lou arranged for an Uber to take her from Soho to Westminster. There was no way she was tackling the Underground in a pair of shoes with one heel hanging on for dear life. It could have been worse.

It could have snapped right off. At least it was still attached and they could pass for a normal pair of shoes till she got up to his room. Fortunately, no one on reception noticed her putting less weight on her left foot as she meandered in, collected her key and made her way up.

Warren had indicated that he was game for any surprise, but Lou reiterated it would just be her. She wanted to manage his expectations and didn't want him to be disappointed when she arrived solo. He said he would probably be asleep, but she knew that was a lie. A little tipsy, Lou entered his suite. All the lights were off apart from a sidelight in the lounge area. It helped guide her to the bathroom, where she used the loo and removed her dress. It was a shame he wouldn't see it, but it meant she could wear it another time with him, perhaps when they went out for dinner. Lou's rugby friends had already commented on it and were surprised she'd worn such a sexy number for work, so all was not lost.

Down to a matching two-set and heels, Lou wandered into the bedroom, where Warren was laying on his side 'asleep'. He was barely lit from the other room, but she could make him out clearly. Lou knelt down next to him and began to kiss the shoulder that was exposed. He moaned ever so gently as she made her way up to his neck and back down again. No words were spoken. Along his arm she continued to kiss and then lifted up the cover. He was naked beneath the sheets, and he was getting excited. Caressing his skin with her hair, she made her way to her prize, which was growing before her. He adjusted his position so Lou could take him in her mouth. "Oh god, oh god." He whimpered. "Oh yes." Warren was certainly more trusting of her now, as his cock was being kissed and licked in delight. There was no sign of his hand coming across to protect his manhood and she knew he felt way more comfortable with her.

Lou spent enough time awakening his throbbing beast that it was now easy to climb aboard and ride him deeply. Being a rubbish condom applier, she opened the packet and handed it to Warren. It was soon on, even with his eyes shut.

Lou had forgotten about his words of content and the noises he made when enjoying their sex. It made her smile. Lou knew she was in amongst the best sexual partners he had ever encountered, and she relished the thought. It came as a surprise when he admitted later that night that she was top of that list and she couldn't help but give a fist pump whilst straddled his cock with her juices running down his balls.

As was usual with this passionate pair, they were all over the hotel suite, and it was some two hours before they admitted defeat and came to rest. Throughout their entwining, Warren continued to describe what he wanted and how they could explore other scenarios together, all the time telling her he wanted to claim her back after she'd been with other people. To Lou, this seemed the perfect arrangement. As he admitted, she did have an insatiable appetite. He described her as always needing more and more cock. What better way for her to be his than for him to fuck another man out of her after she'd had sex with someone else? Lou could certainly see no issue with this setup.

"I'd like to be asleep with you laying next to me, snuggled up close. While I'm sleeping, someone is taking you from behind and you're nudging into me as he fucks you. This wakes me up. You don't see who he is. He just fucks you, comes and then he leaves." It was a similar conversation to one they had recently. This was obviously playing on Warren's mind. All of this talk was turning Lou on too. Grinding against his leg, Lou said, "What, like this?" Warren was immediately aroused. "Yes. Just like that. He's sliding it into you and you're rubbing up against me. You'd like that, wouldn't you?" 'Hell yes', she thought. Bloody right she would. Lou agreed. "Yes, I'd fucking love that." "Do you want me to arrange it?" he asked. A split second was all it took. "Yes, I would. But they have to be fit, and they have to use protection." Warren said he would naturally ensure both of those requirements were met. Lou didn't know when for, but she didn't doubt he would do his utmost to sort it out. Warren was a little impulsive she had grown to learn of late.

As was usual, they had to really try hard to leave each other alone after they'd finished having sex. It was all too easy for one or both of them to start caressing again and before they knew it, he'd be balls-deep in her and they'd be thrashing around once more. Finally, they settled at around 2am. Wow - what a night it had been. Talk about cram everything in. Lou very quickly fell into a deep sleep.

CINNAMON TWIST

With the alarm set for 6.30am, this gave Lou enough time for some morning sex before she set off for the office. She woke naturally some twenty minutes before that and was surprised to see the bathroom light on. That was odd. Usually if Warren were awake before her, his hands would have already been all over her and she'd be dripping wet by now. Lou thought he must have needed to use the toilet. In the back of her mind though, she did wonder if he'd set up the scenario they'd spoken about just a few hours before - surely not? It was only four hours ago after all.

Warren came back to the bed and lay down next to her. Again, he kept to himself, which was different from his normal behaviour. 'Oh boy,' Lou wondered. Had he been plotting during the night? Lou got up and went to the toilet. It was best that she was prepared just in case. She left the bathroom light on as she came back and snuggled up next to him. He was already playing with himself quite vigorously. Fuck, this really must be happening!

Less than two minutes later, Lou heard the hotel door open. Someone was coming in. OMG! Bloody hell! Fuck! She moved even closer to Warren. "Wow. You did it! I can't believe it. Am I allowed to see him?" She had so many thoughts racing around her mind. "Up to you," he responded, still furiously pulling his penis. Lou contemplated whether she wanted to see who this visitor was. Would it be better never to know? Would that be even kinkier than seeing her penetrator? She decided she wouldn't look at him. It would be sexier to be fucked by a faceless stranger

81

and always be left wondering.

They heard the wrapper being opened on a fresh condom box. Warren kept an eye on him and made sure he put the protection on. Grinding up against his right leg, Lou prepared for the taking. She was supercharged and wanting to fulfil Warren's fantasy. The third party licked his hand, slid it up inside her pussy ensuring she was ready and then he plunged in deep. Lou gasped (probably a little louder for effect, although she was incredibly horny) and leaned more heavily against Warren. As each thrust was taken, she rubbed into him more. Warren was wanking and moaning as she did. It was victorious all round. Warren was living out his fantasy and Lou was doing something incredibly horny that she'd never done before.

Lou was in awe of Warren. How he'd managed to set this naughtiness up so quickly was madness. It was also a massive turn on! This was different from any MMF (male, male, female) Lou had experienced before, and she loved this new dimension.

Unfortunately for their guest, the excitement was just a little too much for him to take. He pulled Lou over so she was on her back and he slammed into her till he came hard. At this point, she did look up and noticed his trim physique. (Warren had not let her down.) She couldn't make out his face, just his silhouette, as it was still quite dark in the room. Lou caught herself trying to study his features, so she closed her eyes. She'd already decided she didn't want to know what he looked like, so why was she trying to fathom it out?

CINNAMON TWIST

The stranger had been given very clear instructions by Warren, and that included when he finished he was to collect his things and leave. So after reaching climax, he slowly withdrew, holding the filled condom in place and retreated to the bathroom.

Lou and Warren were both buzzing with adrenaline and desire. Warren climbed on top and told her how he needed to fuck the other guy out of her. "You liked that, didn't you? You dirty bitch. Now I'm going to claim you back." He pummeled Lou for a while and then told her to get on top. She assumed the position eagerly and began to push down onto him, deeper and deeper till Lou continued until she could get no further. They were both fuelled with passion from the earlier encounter and she came all over him a number of times. The bed was getting steadily saturated the more she rode. The pair of them laughed as their guest was still in the bathroom and had helped himself to a shower while they continued. They wondered just how long he was going to be in there! Fortunately, it wasn't much longer.

Even after he left, the passionate pair carried on. Warren told her he had lined up a big black cock too, just in case the first man didn't show up. "Bloody hell Warren. You don't mess about." He was certainly driven! Just then the hotel telephone began to ring. Warren got up to answer it and then returned to the side of the bed, and Lou began to demonstrate her oral skills. Nothing else was said. Still, in a state of shock with the first visitor, Lou couldn't quite get her head around the fact that

83

another was lined up and was very likely to arrive at any moment. She was right!

Once more the door opened, and she could feel a male presence behind her. As she continued to suck Warren, two huge arms were suddenly wrapped around her legs and someone behind her plunged his tongue inside her pussy. It was exciting, but it was a little too aggressive. The angry slurping noises were enough to put her and Warren off. He looked down at her with a 'is everything all right?' expression and she indicated that it was a bit much. With both arms in the air, she motioned to 'calm down'. Warren immediately pulled Lou towards him and told the man to go a bit easier. Before he was about to resume his lapping, Warren asked him if he had a condom. To their surprise, he did not. "I have a cock ring. Can I put this on? It vibrates." That was enough of an early warning to Warren. Who expects to go to a meet without any protection? "No mate. Sorry. You can go. Go on fuck off!"

To his credit, the now unwanted male did get up and looked like he was going to leave. Warren resumed the missionary position and was soon inside Lou, both laughing quietly about how badly the second episode had gone. Lou still felt uneasy as their discredited guest hadn't left the room and asked Warren to escort him out. She just had a funny feeling about him still being around, and Lou always went with her instincts. They were usually right. Warren agreed. He got up to check the guy was going, only to find he was still lingering in their room, watching them and wanking. "Go on mate.

84

Time to go," he said. Lou expected that to be it, but instead, he said, "Please, can I eat your woman just one more time?" Ewww, grim, she thought. "No mate. Now fuck off," and this time he did.

Thank goodness for that! Now they could finally finish what they started. Reminiscing about this naughty morning, they were both able to reconnect and come to orgasm rather quickly. Warren's display was particularly explosive all over her breasts. He'd been building that up as another of his fantasies became a reality with his new naughty partner. Lou looked forward to bringing more of them to fruition if this was the sort of exhilaration they manifested.

Lou bounced off to work with a beaming smile on her face and a naughty glow in her knickers. No one would ever believe the experience she had this morning. What an incredible way to start the day!

Chapter 7 – Cuckold in the making

"Would it turn you on if I got men in for you at my place and they fucked you while I watched?" Paul was testing the water with Lou to gauge her reaction. Lou's immediate thought was "what the fuck?" But she knew how much she adored male attention and this was sounding very promising. "How'd you mean? Tell me more." Paul went on to describe in great detail this fantasy of his. He wanted to do this for Lou's benefit and to make himself jealous: he would try to seek new men for her sexual entertainment.

"What about if I had a dick enlargement? Would that turn you on?" It was his next question. Lou was confused. "But there's nothing wrong with your dick." She told him, and there wasn't. He had managed to satisfy her already. It was a little thin, but certainly reached all the right places and had Lou gushing all over him when she rode. "I could make it thicker, with more girth. I'd go under the knife if it would turn you on." Lou was a little worried. This was an extreme measure and she didn't want to be a part of it. "No babe. That wouldn't turn me on. I don't think you need it." 'There,' Lou thought, 'that felt better'.

"Ok, so would it turn you on if I cut off all ties with Lisa, my ex?" Lou was wondering where this one was going and was a little confused. "I'm sorry. Why would that turn me on?" Paul explained that Lou would be the only lady he would then be thinking of. There would be no chance of him making contact with Lisa then. He would be devoted to Lou. Once more Lou found this rather unsettling. "No, it's fine. I don't mind you still being in touch with her. Just don't fuck her."

The line of questioning continued for the next two hours. A little drained already, Lou wanted to sleep, but this was all too intriguing. Initially she found it quite difficult to keep this conversation up, but after a while she treated it like role-play and settled into it. She then found herself reeling off her responses quite easily.

"What about my flatmate? Would you fuck him in front of me just to make me jealous?" Now Lou had seen his cohabitant and he wasn't her type. She declined but asked if Paul had some hot friends who could do this with instead. He did have. He suggested that she have fun with them but under the pretence that Paul knew nothing about it. Lou agreed to this. "And I'd fuck you after?" she asked. Paul's idea was to have oral with her straight after and taste them on her once they had left. (It reminded her of Warren.) Then, if she let him, he would have intercourse with her. "Oh, and they'd have to bring you gifts of course." Ok, so this was taking a different turn, but she would play along and see where it was going.

As well as his circle of male friends, Paul thought he could summon up a regular supply of other fit and handsome men for Lou (*like she couldn't find her own*). These would probably be his business clients who would have to pay for the privilege of having Lou and Paul would insist they had to bring presents for her too! There was an element of fascination for Lou. She wondered exactly how far this could go and her materialist spark was ignited, even though she wasn't sure how realistic these scenarios were.

"What gifts would you like from them?" Lou thought on her feet. Paul had already offered to buy her shoes, bags, perfume and anything else she wanted (not that any had been forthcoming yet). "Well you seem to be buying me gifts already, so they can contribute to my wardrobe collection." It seemed like a reasonable solution. Lou did like latex, but it was very expensive, so this is where his associates could financially step up to the mark.

"I don't ever want to come again unless you allow me to." Paul wanted Lou to be in control of his orgasms. Only she would permit them, and that meant when together and apart. He was not allowed to masturbate unless she allowed it and it could be weeks before she did. He could not have sex with another woman unless Lou said he could.

It was agreed that if he were good, Lou would permit him to wank or have another woman, but it would cost him. "Would that turn you on?" He repeated. "If you say I can, then I'll buy you something beautiful. But if you say I can't, then I will have to control it and not touch my cock until you let me." Lou reminded him that she would sometimes not see him for weeks. Could he seriously manage that long without coming? "For you, of course, I will. I'll have to." And so the deal was sealed, or so she thought.

The conversation was soon exhausted, as were their energy levels. They decided to call it a day and get some rest. Lou returned home later that evening and reflected on their somewhat unusual discussions.

A few days passed and Lou heard nothing from Paul. She really was unsure where she stood. Was this agreement in place? Was he already declining himself masturbation or was the arrangement made under the influence of something stronger than gin and prosecco? Lou had nothing else that night, but she wasn't sure if Paul had taken anything stronger. It may well have been drug-induced bullshit.

"So, I'm just wondering, about the conversations we had and if we are actually live with what agreed?" Given the in-depth discussions, Lou was convinced he would know exactly what she was getting at, but he was very vague. "We spoke about a lot of things on Sunday. What exactly are you referring to?" Lou thought it was a cop out and didn't pursue it. 'Fair enough,' she thought. She would leave it there, so she was surprised to hear from him a week after they originally spoke about it. It was another Sunday morning and Lou had her children in the house. Paul messaged, "Can I call you please?" She told him her kids were there, so the conversation may be a little one-sided, but she could sense some sort of desperation.

"I had a dream that you put me out to work. You made me have sex with men and then I gave you all my earnings." 'Well, this was very strange,'

Lou thought. Having told her that he had never had sex with a man before, Lou wondered if he was looking for some excuse to explore his bisexuality or homosexuality. She went along with it.

"Is this something you want to try Paul?" She should have anticipated his response, which was, "Only if it will turn you on. Would it turn you on?" Lou was a little surprised with the subject of this phone call but again was curious as to where it would lead. "Yes Paul, it would." He asked her if she would set up an online profile for him, but Lou told him to set up his own, which he did as they spoke.

In completing his profile, Lou was faced with answering all the questions for him, about how much he should charge, whether he should allow them to come in his mouth, if they could bring friends and if he would let them blindfold him, to name but a few. Lou ensured all her answers had health and safety in mind, both from a physical perspective as well as from sexually transmitted diseases. She didn't want him harmed in any way.

Paul's ultimate mission was for Lou to be as turned on as possible and to earn her up to £100,000 for a year's work. He would even give her an allowance and access to his savings if it would turn her on.

Lou could tell he was getting aroused as he was playing with his cock while tailoring his online presence. "Am I allowed to come yet? I haven't since you left here last week and I'm afraid I am going to pop." Oh, so the arrangement was in place. No formal agreement seemed to have been reached, but it appeared that it was active. "I didn't realise you were engaged in this. You didn't seem to be too keen when we last spoke of it." Lou reminded him. "I haven't come because you haven't told me I could. I've been holding it all in. I haven't even touched myself." Talk about bloody confusing!

Because Paul had set up his profile and that he made all those promises to her, Lou said she would let him come. Frantically after that Lou could hear him wanking. "Does that turn you on, Lou? I will only come for you." "Then you must come now, Paul. You have been very good. Now let it all out." It was just the trigger he needed. A loud gasp came shooting out of her handset as he spilt his overdue load all over himself.

After some time on the phone, Lou did wonder if she had in fact become the worst-earning sex chat line ever. She was obviously doing it wrong! Again she had entertained his fantasies on the phone and received nothing back in return, apart from promises of financial gain, which appeared to be unsubstantiated. He had offered to give up his own business to focus on making money for Lou and set her up with a credit card from his account, but again nothing seemed forthcoming.

It had certainly been educational for Lou. Paul was the first cuckold man she had in-depth talks with on this subject. She would have liked to see both arrangements through to fruition - Paul finding men for her and him working for her too. Lou wanted to find out if she was comfortable having sex in front of him and knowing it would make him jealous, and how that scenario would pan out, but Lou had her doubts.

Taking control of his orgasms did appeal, as she wanted to explore the BDSM side a little more and push some new boundaries there. But maybe this was all in Paul's active imagination rather than reality, which Lou felt was a shame. It wasn't even about the financial gain, but given the time she had wasted on the phone to him, then a reward on some scale would have been welcomed. Lou's education in the cuckold world would have to be put on pause until she found one that was truly serious.

Chapter 8 – Pay per shot

"Are you English?" he began. It was a different website Lou had not used before. She was keen to explore another, as the one she had been on for a while was becoming a little tedious. The continuous flow of "Hi, how are you?" approaches were getting boring, so she thought she'd try a new one.

"Yes, I am English," she responded. Lou was sure she had filled this information in when she set up the profile, but she may be mistaken. She remembered recording she was 'white and Caucasian.' He, on the other hand, was Emirate and would only be in the UK once or twice a month. This would increase soon as he was setting up a business in London.

"We adore the white flesh. Would you consider outsourcing?" Well this was an unusual question, Lou thought, but it certainly sparked her curiosity. She was keen to understand where this was leading to, although she had a pretty good idea. Now adopting the role, she continued to play along. "And who would the outsourcing be to exactly?" He advised it would be his business associates and colleagues. Alarm bells were starting to ring in Lou's head, but she carried on to see how this would evolve.

"How many business associates and colleagues would be in attendance?" Lou was surprised to learn this figure would be between ten to fifteen men. "And during what time frame?" Up to three hours, he revealed. She was beginning to feel her skin crawl ever so slightly. "Would Viagra be permitted?" He confirmed it would. "And all safe?" Again he agreed this to be the case. They would all be wearing extra thick condoms apparently.

He went on to tell her that she would be compensated for her efforts to the sum of '£500 per shot.' Lou wanted clarification. She asked if that meant 'per load' and he confirmed that was exactly what he meant. Immediately the sums were being made in her head. So basically, Lou could earn up to £7,500 for a few hours fucking - not that she had any intention of doing so, but it was certainly a profitable prospect. If Lou didn't do it, there definitely would be a long line of other girls out there who would do.

What fascinated Lou about all of this was the fact that it was all just there at her fingertips – quite literally. Her mobile phone gave Lou access to this other world in which she could be paid for sex with strangers on mass! It was all very interesting and yet appalling to her all at the same time. Lou wasn't sure how she felt about it, but she couldn't help but carry on the pretence.

It was getting late. Lou had work the next morning, and she felt she'd had enough of this conversation. She put her phone on charge and got some sleep, although this was playing on her mind a little. She felt a little unsettled about the conversation that had taken place.

The next day he soon contacted her again. He was keen to know she was ok and wanting to carry on where they left off. He continued with, "How many has the vessel taken in one sitting?" So now she was a vessel. How charming! He was interested in the number of men Lou had fucked in one session. Lou was not prepared to tell him anything that personal, so she made up a figure and said "seven men and one woman." He was interested then in the ages of those involved, to gauge how fit Lou was and how capable she was of servicing the men he would bring for her. "I may have miscalculated. I may have to bring in another vessel to assist with load-bearing." Why was Lou surprised? The matter-of-fact way in which he was speaking was rather discerning. Respect and morals were not required in this interview process!

Continuing with the role she asked, "How does one vet the outsourcees?" Lou was curious to know. It transpired that he was developing an online application purely for this purpose. It was being designed for darker skinned men to choose white-fleshed women and pay them for sex. It was already in use in Dubai and Poland, and he was expanding into the UK. Ultimately, Lou would have control over which men would be the willing participants in this novel transaction (should she choose to go through with this). It gave her some say at least (again, all hypothetically).

Lou had less time to message him on this particular evening. She had her kids at home and didn't want to waste their time together with her being on her phone all night. It was refreshing to leave the technology on the side and spend some quality time with them instead. Too soon it had an ability to distract her and that wasn't fair.

The next day Lou got another distressing message from him. "Lou, where are you? Are you ok? Shall we carry on discussing the outsourcing arrangement and how we can make this work?" Lou found this a little creepy, to say the least. "Well, to be honest, I'm not ok. I did fear for the safety of the vessel." He seemed a little shocked. "But you would vet the attendees via the app. There is nothing to fear. I will meet all men personally beforehand when they pay to list on my site. It is part of the membership process. I will make sure they are respectful and can pay."

"So where does one download the app?" Lou was still curious all the same, to be told that she would only get the app once he had a 'test drive'. 'Oh here we go,' Lou thought. "Ok, so who does the quality assurance for the test-drive?" She asked him, knowing full well what the answer would be. "Well that would be me," he retorted. Well that was no surprise, was it?

"Do I get to see what you look like?" Lou realised he had not shown her any pictures of himself. Lou had provided him with a couple of tasteful photos of her own. They did show her face and figure, but all fully clothed and revealing very little flesh. When his pictures came across, Lou felt disgusted. There was no way she would have sex with him, not for any monetary value. He was not her type whatsoever and she never went with anyone she didn't fancy.

With regard to his business associates and colleagues, she was pretty sure they would all look very similar to him. She doubted they would be respectful, despite what he said previously. Lou couldn't help but think of a broken, likely bleeding 'vessel' being found crying in a hotel room and quite possibly needing reconstructive surgery of her bits and pieces. It was not a very nice thought, but one she could easily imagine, all too scarily. She wondered how many women had thought with pound signs in their eyes and gone along with this sort of arrangement? It sounded dangerous. It sounded sordid, but then she could also see the appeal particularly for someone who had debts to pay or needed some hard cash fast.

Lou didn't message him again and she never heard back from him either. It seems he did not require her delicate white flesh after all. He must have found a different vessel to use, or a number of them, which quite frankly came as no disappointment to Lou, but she did find the whole experience quite enlightening, to say the least. It made her question her morals, but thankfully she came away thinking she was happy with her decision not to pursue this prospect any further, how ever much money was involved.

CINNAMON TWIST

Chapter 9 – Introducing the Master

Lou met Master D with her friends at a pub in Henley. She had no idea he was a dominatrix (dom) when she first began speaking with him, but then why would she? Not all doms hit their local alehouse in their best spanking outfit, well not that she imagined.

Lou's friends were off to a sex club after their initial drinks, and Natalie wondered if she would care to join them. Of course she would. Lou had spent nights with them before at gatherings they had hosted which had been exciting and naughty for all involved. Natalie's playmate tended to enjoy watching the girl on girl action before he would get involved. It was quite a turn on knowing he was staring at them from just outside the room, secretly peeking in, hoping not to be caught. Lou had glanced across a few times during their encounters and spied him. His presence would be more evident when she was giving or being given oral pleasure. 'Dirty boy,' Lou thought, but she did kind of like it too.

Natalie introduced Lou to Master D as they were queuing at the bar for drinks. Standing a good 6' 8", he was huge compared with her, even with her four-inch heeled boots on. He was an enigmatic character too with the personality to match. He was much more rotund than anyone Lou had ever slept with before – even more so than her ex-husband, so she found it quite unusual when she discovered herself beginning to flirt with him. He wasn't her normal type whatsoever, well apart from the height perhaps. Lots of her rugby friends stood over six feet – well most of them!

Master D was certainly on the charm-offensive and Lou found him a delight to be around. He was intelligent and funny, and when he came to reveal more about himself, Lou was hooked. Not only was he dominant, but he was also a master dom who had his own 'play space' that he rented out to other female financial dominatrices. He made it very clear that this was not a dungeon, although it had all the equipment and more, without the sordid association of such an area made for pleasure.

Master D recalled many of his hilarious experiences in the BDSM world, as well as poignant tales of how people had truly released themselves to him. Lou was captivated, particularly as she had frequently been asked of late whether she was dom or 'sub' (submissive). Lou found herself hanging on his every word.

Following a few drinks in the pub, they shared a cab to the club. As was more often the norm than not, where they were headed had no alcohol license, so they would have to stop off on route to pick up some drink. Master D picked up a couple of bottles of champagne and they were now suitably armed. Whether it was intentional or not, he was doing well to impress them; Lou in particular.

Inside they ran into a few couples they knew from the venue. Lou had played with one couple there before, and they just so happened to know the people she went along with on this occasion. 'The swinging world can be so small at times!' Lou thought. She guessed that the more time you spent in it, the more chances there were of bumping into people you knew (or your friends knew) or people you had fucked (or your friends had)!

Lou wasn't that fussed about playing tonight. She was feeling a little tipsy and decided she wasn't on the prowl. She had her prey here and he was the larger than life Master D before her. Lou explained to him that she was keen to embark on her own dominant journey and asked if he would guide her. He was the expert here and she valued his wisdom and experience, but as soon as she made the request, she felt immediately silly. How many times must he be asked that she wondered? She hoped she hadn't insulted him or ruined her chances. Thankfully Master D was receptive to the idea and it was something they could pursue together. He would happily mentor her. 'Phew!' she thought. 'Thank goodness for that!' The last thing she wanted to do was upset a dom!

As their conversation continued, Lou described her preferences during sex and they established that she had more dominant tendencies than submissive. "What you need to do is to understand exactly what your sub is going through. The only way you'll get it is to feel how the sub feels - to experience both sides of it. I know just the man who would be very happy to help you with this too." Immediate nerves and trepidation shot through Lou's body. She had no real sub tendencies that she could think of other than enjoying a man throwing her around the bedroom a little, but wasn't that more about being in the company of a strong male than being sub? Lou enjoyed being teased, but again she wasn't sure if this constituted being sub. Being outside of her comfort (or more likely 'control') zone would be a challenge for her, but it was one she was willing to try just to experience it entirely. It was all about pushing boundaries after all.

Lou and Master D were inseparable, animatedly discussing the various escapades they had encountered. This must have become evident to others because while they were deeply engrossed, Natalie whispered in her ear, "Why don't we go and have some fun in the cage?" They must have been neglecting the others!

The cage was a room with an elevated bed area, surrounded by walls on two sides and bars on the other two, with a lockable door. It meant that sex could take place inside while voyeurs had access through to the action. Equally, those in the cage could reach out and interact if they chose to.

Natalie led Lou by the hand and off the ladies went, giggling as they did so. It wasn't long before they were followed and the show began. Men and women gathered outside of the cage and watched. Both ladies stripped off to their underwear once inside and deposited their clothes in a corner. They ignored the signs to remove their heeled shoes and began their play.

As usual, Natalie was incredibly sensitive and responsive. It wasn't long before she was quivering and gasping in delight with Lou's head buried deep between her legs. Lou was always surprised how quickly Natalie came. In some respects, she was quite jealous and could only imagine exploding that fast. But then again, Lou also liked to draw it out gradually and savour that slow building orgasm. It really depended on the situation and whom she was with.

Natalie pushed Lou off when it became too much as she came hard for all to see. She made some delightful squirms and moans, much to the enjoyment of those around them.

As she was recovering, Lou turned to Master D who was standing up against the bars. She told him to unbutton his trousers. She wanted to have his cock in her mouth through the bars and he appeared to be very excited to oblige. His flies were just fully opened as the lights went on in the room. What was going on? It was time to go. The club was closing. "Nooo!" Lou thought. Just as it was all getting very interesting. She was gutted. Damn! She would have to wait until they got back to Henley. Just how long had they been chatting in the other room exactly? Where had tonight gone? How was it now 3am already?

There seemed to be a mutual disappointment, although Natalie was certainly looking pleased with herself! They gathered up their belongings, put on the stray clothing and made their way to the reception, where a cab was ordered for them. Much to Lou's surprise, Master D bid her farewell in the cab and left the threesome to their own devices once they were safely delivered back to Henley.

He showed all the attributes of a true gentleman as he told her it had been a pleasure to meet her and hopefully their paths would cross again. They exchanged numbers and Lou said she looked forward to it. However, sadly, it would take some five months to pass before she saw him again.

Chapter 10 – Prague escape

Even though their careers had taken different paths some years before, Snake Hips and Lou had always kept in touch. They had become long-distance friends with benefits, who met when he visited London, which was around every few months. They had also met in some far-flung countries when their business travel calendars collided. It all added to the adventure of their on/off relationship.

Prague was different. It was a planned excursion from two different cities with a combined intention – to have a lot of naughty pleasure abroad, consisting of three nights in a city they had both visited but separately before.

Their flights arrived at the Czech Republic just twenty minutes apart. Lou walked through the airport first and waited on the other side of arrivals. Even though she knew he would be a few minutes yet, she couldn't help but look at every single person that came through after her.

Finally (after what seemed like way longer than the scheduled time) there he was. He was beaming from ear to ear as their eyes met. Oh, this was exciting! He was almost running as he brushed past a few people to get to her sooner. Then they were in each other's arms again. It was like a scene from a film, only without any cheesy music to accompany it. They were all hugs and kisses before he put Lou down and they composed themselves. They felt like naughty school children absconding from work and their usual lives.

Lou had booked the accommodation, as he couldn't have it showing up on his bank account. His wife would not exactly approve, so Lou took care of it. He would reimburse her later. It was a fairly reasonable hotel, right in the heart of the city, where they could walk to all the shops, which they planned to do once their taxi delivered them safely and they had checked in.

They were both a little hungry, so the intention was to drop their bags and get straight out there for food and exploration. However, that wasn't exactly how it played out. No sooner had her bag touched the floor of their hotel room that he was on her. His desire was strong, and he picked her up out of the bathroom and carried her to the bed. She unwrapped her legs from around his waist as she was flung on top of the quilt where she kicked off her boots.

Snake Hips' kissing began furiously: on her lips, her neck and chest, working his way downwards. His hands grasped at her jeans, opening the button and pulling them down in haste. He wanted to taste her and he wanted it right now! Jeans around her knees, knickers tangled up inside them, his mouth was searching as he pushed her legs apart. Lou hadn't expected this but was now oh so pleased his desire had taken hold.

Snake Hips was developing a rhythm with his tongue on her clit. He knew just how Lou liked it: a slobbery soft tongue lashing left to right, over and over, then sliding a finger inside her. Oh yeah, that was it. She could feel her orgasm building up. Her back was beginning to arch as he was certainly hitting her button all right! It wasn't much longer and there it was. Boom! Damn, he was good.

Lou didn't have time to recover. She just about managed to drag her jeans past her right foot so she could be more mobile. At least one leg was out now. It didn't matter that her left leg was still clothed. He had full access to where he needed to be and his hard cock was out of his pants and straight inside her. (No time was wasted with condoms. They had a special arrangement where that was concerned and they trusted each other implicitly.)

Snake Hips was rampant and he was now fucking her hard. The pounding was deep and fast and they could feel every sensation. Lou knew it wouldn't take long for him to come. She doubted he'd have had sex with his wife before he came out to Prague, so it had probably been building up for a while. Lou was right. He was pulling that determined face she recognised and his concentration was locked in. Either he was focussing on not ejaculating yet, or he was happy to let his climax develop naturally. It was hard to tell, but he was definitely on his way!

A few more controlled thrusts and Snake Hips was ready to burst. He whipped his penis out of her and exploded his spunk all over her stomach, growling all the way as the euphoria swept through him. Whoa, that was a big one! Lou was covered (and soon back in the bathroom for a shower)!

106

Out then for some drinks and food before they plotted their next move. Snake Hips had researched the alternative nightlife and found a swingers' club in the outskirts of town. It might be worth a little closer inspection. The reviews online certainly looked promising and they decided they would try it out the following night. Today was more about settling in, catching up and sharing each other's bodies. After a few more cocktails, they did exactly that.

The next day was a buzz of excitement as they did some more shopping, this time for underwear for the club tonight. Snake Hips was keen to buy her something new for the occasion and they settled on a black two-set that they both particularly liked. Lou felt super sexy wearing it and he couldn't wait to have her in it and then out of it.

This horny pair couldn't get enough of each other. It was addictive! The plan had been to save themselves for the club, but post-shopping again they stole some time to get naked and entwined before they got ready to go out.

After a few drinks close to their hotel, they jumped in a cab and gave the driver the address. He didn't seem too keen and certainly was not very smiley. Maybe that was just his way, but he could have benefited from some customer service training. When his satnav indicated they were at their destination, he pulled over to the side of the road and couldn't take their money quick enough. Snake Hips asked him for directions after that to the club, but he feigned not being able to understand him. That was all a little strange.

CINNAMON TWIST

To add to the air of mystery and discomfort, the area he had dropped them in was on the outskirts of town. It seemed like quite a run-down place and Lou immediately thought of the old Tarantino film 'Hostel'. Thank goodness for Google Maps, which gave them an idea of what direction to walk in. They now found themselves at a residential block of flats. Surely this couldn't be right? It seemed like the last place they'd find a swingers club.

Given they were all dressed up, including Lou in a skin-tight, somewhat revealing dress and heels, they could not have felt more out of place. That was until they saw another couple in similar attire. They were surely going to the same place, so they decided to follow them. It wasn't far at all; just around the other side of the building.

What can only be described as a loading bay, with a metal staircase attached, is where they spied any form of connection. Scribbled on a square of cardboard was the name of the club taped to the door. It also had a black arrow pointing to a different doorbell. They appeared to be in the right place, albeit a little shambolic. (Lou wondered how on earth people with disabilities would ever get in here. Her friend Daz often asked her about swingers clubs and their facilities and how anyone in a wheelchair would get about inside. Well, he would have had a lot of problems here!)

The pair they were following slipped quietly in. Lou and Snake Hips were not far behind them as they made their way up the stairs. They weren't exactly easy for her either in those heels, wanting to scrape and fall through the holes wrecking them in the process. She tiptoed up, with her arm firmly gripping on to her hunky lover. He would protect her! He was trained to after all! They rung the bell and were expecting a door buzzing release sound as they pushed their way through. However that was not the case. Instead, a voice greeted them in Czech and it was one they did not understand. They tried the door at the same time, but it was still firmly locked.

A moment later and the door was opened from the inside. A strapping man easily standing six feet four inches popped his head out to greet them initially and realised they were not locals when Snake Hips tried talking to him. He did not understand but beckoned for them to follow him. Again, with 'Hostel' running through her mind, she clung to her man as they entered. The closer she was to him the better in Lou's mind.

Her fears were soon destroyed when they were guided to the main bar area. A stunning (and almost equally tall) woman came up to them and asked if they were English. 'Was it obvious?' Lou wondered. They explained they were and it was the first time to a swingers club in Prague. She revealed she was the owner and looked thrilled that they had come to her club. She offered them a drink and once settled offered to show them around the facilities, including the lockers where they would be depositing their belongings and clothes. (Seemed the lovely new underwear would get another display, but not here as it was not the policy, so they would have to wait until they were back at the hotel.)

CINNAMON TWIST

There was a good vibe in the club, although it was still relatively early and not many visitors yet. On the tour, Lou noticed the club was similar to others she had visited in various countries. It was the usual set up with various play rooms (some with doors to remain closed, others could stay open), there was a large jacuzzi and a dungeon area with all sorts of contraptions and toys. They passed the small kitchen area on the way, with a buffet on display for them to tuck into as and when they wished. The entrance ticket included all drinks and food, which meant they didn't have to carry anything around with them all night.

The main meeting area in front of the bar consisted of a seated area to the left with numerous sofas. To the right there was a dance floor separated by a chain metal curtain with a raised step containing three separate poles, one of which was set to spinning whilst the other two were fixed on static. Lou would no doubt be up on one of those later!

They left their drinks at the bar as they went off to de-robe. All items were placed inside the lockers and swapped for the towels they found there. Once duly adorned, they made their way back to the main room.

As they sipped on their incredibly strong drinks and having made small talk with the owner, they made their way to the sofas. People were starting to trickle in now, and they both wanted to check out any talent as they walked in. It was the usual hunting ground moment, which occurred in every club Lou had been to, where everyone sizes each other up for later play potentiality.

Their conversation was focused on the eagerness of the night and not knowing how it would pan out. Would they find another couple? Would it be another single person who joined them – male or female? It was hard to say. One thing they were set on was playing, even if it was just with each other.

When one rather attractive couple sat on the sofa to the side of them, Lou and Snake Hips quickly did an assessment. The young man had a very fit body whereas she was a little bigger in frame and possibly a little curvier than he was used to. She really could have done with a bigger towel as her voluptuous bosom was fighting to stay inside. They both had lovely faces and would certainly be considered as the night went on.

The club was gradually filling up and another couple struck up a conversation with them. They were locals and their English was very good. They had arrived when the club opened, consumed their dinner there and already used the facilities. They were now interested in getting drunk and possibly repeating the latter in this process. But Lou and Snake Hips were not interested in joining them on their second round. They did not appeal to their carnal desires and the wet couple soon moved on to another sofa where they tried their efforts again.

Lou found she was getting attention from a number of single males in the club who came and sat on the seat opposite them. She was unsure what their policy on unaccompanied men but there appeared to be a few here this evening. Snake Hips wasn't in any way threatened. If anything, he was quite encouraging of Lou having another man join the two of them in a room. He was very keen and was vetting them as they spoke with Lou.

While she enjoyed the chatting, there was only really one other guy in there that she was attracted to and that was the one from the original couple they spied earlier, with the good body. Snake Hips went over and spoke with the couple and asked if they wanted to join them. They had a chat amongst themselves and then decided to come across and talk with them. Lou remarked on his fit physique and 'Steve' said it was nothing compared with her partner's. He was right too. Snake Hips had a fantastic form and he was over ten years older than their new friend.

Steve said he travelled from Dubai and often visited Prague and this club in particular. It was the better of the two in the area, so Lou was pleased with the choice they made. Lou was also convinced that this man was definitely not a 'Steve', but it didn't matter. She understood cultures and it was up to him what pretence he wanted to display for the evening. There was no judgement here.

The female of the two didn't say much. Lou couldn't work out if she wanted to be there or not, as her English wasn't very good and she got the impression she didn't want to speak with them. 'Each to their own,' Lou thought.

A second rather strong drink down and things were starting to heat up. Lou, Snake Hips and Steve were ready to roll and his partner agreed to come into a room, where a glass panel allowed others to watch, but the door would be locked. This didn't bother the English couple in the slightest, and they went with the flow. Both couples played separately to start but on the same bed. Lou's gushing abilities were soon triggered and Steve looked in amazement. His partner was less than thrilled though and soon wanted to leave the room. There was no other explanation other than assuming she did not like this act. Steve stayed regardless and the threesome enjoyed some less restrictive time together.

Lou enjoyed the varieties of spit roast with both men. What a very fit combination of these two lovely specimens! Steve also received a lesson and demonstration in how to perform gushing, which he enjoyed immensely and went home with some new skills! That poor bed! Lou certainly left her mark!

When they finished up in the saturated room, they made their way to the communal showers. There was only really room for two, so Lou and Snake Hips went in and freshened up. Steve followed swiftly behind, and then they moved back to the sofa area. They swapped towels for dry ones and sat down with fresh drinks. That was fun!

Steve's partner was lying on a different sofa and was being pleasured by a couple. The female was tongue-deep inside her vagina and the male was kissing her just before he stuck his cock in her mouth. She seemed ok then. Lou was worried that she would return and find her in a strop. Fortunately, this was not the case, which was a relief.

After a spell on the poles, Lou and Snake Hips decided it was time to call it a day. They asked the owner to call them a cab and once back in their clothes, they waited outside for its arrival. This swiftly brought them back down to earth as they were reminded of their whereabouts. Now it was 2am and they were in a packed but eerily quiet residential car park. It was all very strange and a little dodgy she didn't mind admitting. Lou was relieved to be in the cab and soon back to the hotel.

After another shower, they fell into bed. What a night it had been! She'd already received a Whatsapp from 'Steve' thanking them both for a great night and hoping to see them again sometime in whatever country. He'd obviously had a good night too!

And that was the highlight of their trip to Prague. Lou and Snake Hips were very comfortable together, wherever they were. They had so much in common; their thoughts, morals, actions, principles and humour. What's more is that they were both low maintenance and nothing really phased them. It made trips like this very easy to partake in and they both knew this was not their first, and it would not be their last either. It was just too much fun not to and plans were already afoot for their next one, wherever that may be!

Chapter 11 – Cuckold continued

It was a Saturday morning when Lou discovered a message from Paul. She was a little worse for wear after a heavy night with her rugby pals and some visiting 'unicorns' had joined forces and consumed copious amounts of alcohol before falling into various bedrooms.

Lou hadn't heard from him for a while, so was surprised when he asked her to come and visit him. She wasn't that far away, but she didn't have her car with her. "No matter. I'll send an Uber for you. When are you free?" Lou liked his decisiveness. There was one stipulation: she would have to join the girls for breakfast first and she was glad she did. She felt way more human again when the car arrived for her.

As seemed to be the norm at the moment, Lou had an interesting journey to Paul's house. While chatting to the rather delicious young driver, she discovered they were both on the same sex site and had been to some of the same clubs. Banter exchanged, then numbers too and Lou was safely deposited outside her destination. 'Did this sort of thing happen to other people?' Lou wondered. She wasn't even sure how they got onto the subject, but the formal chitchat soon turned into a conversation about sex. 'Incredible really,' Lou thought and smiled as she made her way to Paul's front door.

Despite the heavily falling snow outside, Paul chose to open the door in his underwear. Lou wandered in. "Jeez, aren't you cold?" she asked him. "I thought you'd like it if I greeted you just in my pants." "I do," she said, "but don't be cold." Lou hated the cold unless she was dressed in multiple layers and toasty warm.

Making her way upstairs to his lounge area, Lou noticed how tidy it was. It looked like he had made an effort. Paul was still using the multiple sofas as a bed and his huge TV was poised on a Google search. His history showed that he had been watching porn, which came as no surprise. She knew he was horny.

Lou sat on his sofa, at which point her phone rang. It was her daughter asking how her night had been. While she took the call, Paul lay on the sofa next to her, scooped his arms around her stomach and placed his head on her lap. Lou stroked his hair tenderly, like he was one of her children, and continued her conversation. She could feel his vulnerability and at the same time the sense of relief he was radiating as she showed him some affection. It did feel a little sad too.

After the call, Lou focussed her undivided attention on him. He had crawled under the covers and she decided to get cosy with him. She stripped down to a strappy vest and knickers, carefully removing her bra as they continued their catch up. She snuggled in with him and they were soon skin on skin, in the spoons position.

CINNAMON TWIST

Paul kissed her neck and wrapped his arms around her as he pulled her in tight. Lou felt him relax as she did the same. His touch was soft and Lou was soon becoming turned on. She had always been a sucker for a bit of neck attention and now was no different, despite still suffering slightly from her overindulgent alcohol binge the night before. This was taking her mind off it. That's for sure. Maybe it was true that sex is good for headaches after all!

It wasn't long before Lou could feel his erection rubbing against her. His penis was long and quite narrow from memory and it was certainly probing all around, but making its way to her special place. It seemed that Paul thought it would be going in there unprotected, but that was not the case. It had been over a month since they had last slept together and whilst Lou had been safe, she wasn't sure if Paul had been, even if he had said he had saved himself for her. How could she really be sure?

Paul had said his cock belonged to Lou only and for that reason, he hadn't fucked anyone since the last time together. He stated that he had been desperate at times, but he had maintained his control, as he knew it would turn Lou on to find this out. This did confuse her slightly as she was never really sure if the two of them were serious about any of their plans from previous discussions. She had also seen his Instagram stories while he'd been away and it appeared he had been having a whole lot of fun, although not necessarily of the bedroom variety. It was hard to tell what he'd been up to, but Lou was not going to risk her health in finding out.

117

Although not 100% safe, it felt more so than bareback intercourse, Lou turned her body around and lowered herself down to his throbbing member and planned on giving him the attention he was now craving – from her mouth that is! As she wormed her way down under the covers he immediately began to sigh. She hadn't even touched him yet! Maybe it had been a while for him after all?

On her way down, Lou kissed his chest, stomach and groin area. They were light kisses followed by her tongue gliding on his skin, carefully avoiding her prize. Paul's body was quivering beneath her and the odd gasp unconditionally escaped him. 'He'd better not come too quickly!' Lou secretly wished to herself. That would be a disappointment.

Lou continued the teasing. She made her way back up to his mouth a few times to kiss him passionately. He was a very good kisser: responsive and equally desire-driven. He was certainly ripe for her and the tip of his cock was continuously leaking. "I can't help it, Lou. There's so much pre-come for you. It's what you do to me. I'm so excited." She used the clear fluid as a lubricant to rub into his helmet and then up and down his shaft. Paul was a quivering mess of excitement as Lou clutched firmly with her hand, then released and gripped even harder. It was sending shock waves through his entire body. "You can be as rough as you like Lou. I can take it - but only if it turns you on. " She had forgotten just how much Paul liked to be dominated. "Oh, I will. Don't you worry about that!" She grabbed him harder and pulled his foreskin down more forcefully. He cried out in pain and pleasure – all merged into one.

This was all very interesting for Lou. She was discovering that in this relationship or whatever this arrangement was, he would suggest ideas but make it look like Lou had thought of them. It was obviously the kink he was into, albeit new for him to act out, and one that Lou realised she could quite happily play a part in.

Lou's attention had already turned to his balls and she was nuzzling her head in them. She had discovered that many men loved this and Paul was no exception. However he did want her to be more brutal with him. "You can pull them hard if you like." Immediately Lou took one ball into her mouth and sucked it hard as she drew it away from his body. The normally saggy sack was dragged upwards and he moaned with the pain when she released it. Lou repeated the process with the other one, even more aggressively this time. She could tell he was getting off on it. "Lou, do you want me to feel you with every stride I make tomorrow? Each shot of pain will remind me of you when I'm walking. Would you like that?" To be honest, Lou didn't have any feelings on this matter. It didn't particularly give her any sense of achievement knowing he would still be suffering a day later. But he seemed to like the idea, so why the hell not? She went along with it and spent the next twenty minutes or so working on this area of his anatomy to new extremes (for her at least).

During a moment's grace, Paul showed Lou how

he wanted her to scoop both balls up in one hand so the other hand could then inflict slaps across the pair. He didn't verbalise this but made it obvious to her by doing it to himself so she could follow his lead. Lou understood the undisclosed instruction and rather easily assumed the new function of scrotum-spanker, slapper, flicker and much more. In fact, Lou found this role very easy to adopt once she got into the mindset. Who knew she was a natural? Well she did have her suspicions and now it seemed, with a little coaching, she found this came as second nature.

What Lou was a little uncomfortable with, were the yelps of pain and the subsidence after that. Lou was normally a very tactile, loving and caring person, so this did feel somewhat out of her comfort zone, but that was what this year was all about. It was about trying new things; pushing boundaries and exploring unchartered territory. It wasn't long before this scenario soon became easy to control. Once Lou relaxed a little more, she felt she was actually enjoying delivering this form of arousal but only because he was blatantly enjoying it so much, despite the cries of pain (followed by sighs of pleasure).

"Would you like to put those sexy boots back on and let me feel them all over me?" There was the subliminal request once more. 'Not really', was her initial thought but she didn't share this with him. 'Ah fuck it, why the hell not?' Lou had heard about guys who liked the stiletto treading onto their delicate areas, squashing, stabbing and the like. "These heels are going to do more than that!" she responded. His face lit up with anticipation. In all honesty, Lou wasn't sure what that meant exactly, but it seemed to have quite a reaction, so she decided to go with it and see where it led.

In true Lou style, before she put her gorgeous footwear anywhere near to him, she decided to nip across to the sink area and give them a quick wash. It was mainly the heels she focused on. She had a feeling one of them may be entering his body at some point and just in case; it should probably be cleaned first. This never seemed to happen in the porn films. There would be no cut to the kitchen sink area, where the leading lady grabbed some kitchen roll, doused it in water and cleaned her boots off before engaging in some sexual activity. It was hardly the most arousing of interludes, but Lou's practical head was reminding her of hygiene. Safety first and all that!

Once her boots had been suitably washed and adorned, Lou crawled onto the sofa. Paul was wanking gently as she straddled him to remind him of skin on skin and then Lou plunged her tongue into his mouth. They kissed deeply for a while, with his cock wanting to enter her but Lou wouldn't allow it. "Tut tut. No babe. It's time for you to become acquainted with my boots." She gracefully moved a little further back from him and pulled her feet closer to his groin area. Lifting her right leg, she slowly dragged the stiletto across his stomach and down to his balls. She could tell it was slightly scratching, but Paul absolutely loved it. Lou did it again and again as he continued to pull his cock up and down.

This was all very well for Paul, but Lou found that lifting her leg up in the air and carefully delivering the motion with such precision was starting to make her thigh ache. She supposed this was good for toning but hadn't expected to be getting this sort of workout today. Lou swapped legs and repeated the action. Always best to do both sides when it came to exercise!

Paul was oblivious to Lou's angst as he nuzzled his head into the cushions. This was hitting the spot. Lou decided to change tactics now and step it up a little - quite literally! Given his delight with her earlier endeavours, she placed the pad of her foot on top of his scrotum and applied pressure. Not only did this provide her thigh with some relief, but it also gave a new dimension to Paul's pleasure/pain experience. "Ooh yeah. That's good. You can go harder if it would turn you on." And that was her cue. She needed no further direction. The ball of her foot met his balls as one, and so the force increased. More moans, cries and gasps ensued as she tried this new approach.

As Lou was rocking her boot to and fro, she guided the stiletto to ever so slightly rub up against his anus. She knew how partial he was to having anything inserted in there, so it seemed like the natural progression in this scene to place her heel up there too - more so knowing how clean her footwear was! Given Lou's disposition, she didn't want it to hurt him really, but she did want him to experience this heightened naughtiness and he was in no way objecting.

It would probably have been easier on him if

CINNAMON TWIST

Lou had smeared some lubricant on his tiny arse, but there was none in the vicinity and he confirmed he didn't have any there. Lou spat on her hand and rubbed it over him. Whilst it wouldn't be as effective, it would at least be better than nothing. Ever so slowly she began the entry. "Shit! That's actually quite sharp." Paul declared. "Do you want me to stop?" Lou questioned. He didn't. He would bear the pain and so, as she squashed his balls, her stiletto met his sphincter.

Paul was tense to start but was soon relaxing into it and joining in with the rhythm she directed. It must have felt incredibly deep for him, as he asked how much of the heel was inside his bum. It was only around one centimetre but it must have felt way more. Lou was ready to withdraw it and concentrate on something new, but Paul had other ideas. "How much further do you want me to take?" Again he was instructing her and she obliged. "Double what it is now." He accepted this 'order' of sorts and Lou continued the slow delving. When it had reached that level, she congratulated him. "Wow. You have done well. It's now at two centimetres. I'm going to pull it out, but I'll take it slowly, so just relax." That was easier said than done. Her heel was sucked in there and this was going to take some care and precision in getting it out. Very delicately Lou withdrew, wiggling slightly to get the final part out and there it was released. 'Phew. Thank fuck for that.' Lou thought as her thigh muscle was almost at the point is spasm. Paul appeared relieved too, bless him. She couldn't blame him! It couldn't have been very comfortable.

Changing positions now, Lou sat upright and tried something new. Paul was playing with his cock as she positioned the arch of her boot sideways, so it engulfed his balls and restricted them to one place. They were now surrounded by her boot. It was a perfect photo opportunity of him restrained by the stiletto and sole of a slutty boot while he grabbed his manhood. This image would be a pleaser for any with a foot fetish or admirers of restraint. Lou happily reached for her iPhone and captured the moment. She would share it with him later and she would allow him wank off to it at a future time. For now, she showed it to him and he approved.

Following this diversion, Lou removed her ball restraining boot and then crept off into the kitchen area. There she washed her defiled footwear once more before casting them both aside and returning to him. His masturbating had taken on a new lease of life as he pondered over what had just happened and probably because his arse was released of any painful protrusion. Lou returned to licking his groin and took his cock in her mouth again.

It was time for Lou to have some pleasure of her own now. "You really need to be inside me, Paul." There were no objections. She reached down to her bag and removed a condom. "Oh we're being sensible are we now?" Lou was instantly reminded of their previous encounter, which was a little irresponsible, but she had been tested since for sexually transmitted diseases and received the all clear. She intended to keep it that way.

It wasn't long before Paul was making new demands while in his submissive state. The irony wasn't lost on Lou, but given she was taking this entire episode as a lesson in domination, she was happy to go with the flow - well, to a point. "Would you like to stick your finger up my arse?" He really did have something about his bum being explored. Again, 'not really' she thought. What she would like now is some pleasure for her. "No Paul. What I'd like now is to crawl on your face and for you to lap up my juices." And she did exactly that. She moved up and straddled his face so he could devour her. It felt good and she was already moist from enjoying the preceding explorations.

His tongue was flicking across her clit and it was causing her to get wetter and wetter. "Hold my nose," he said from beneath her. That was different. Surely that would stop him from breathing? Again Lou complied, but it wasn't long before she became scared of this arrangement. What if he passed out? What if she killed him? This was a step too far out of her comfort zone and she soon released his nostrils. Lou instantly felt at ease. She hadn't enjoyed that at all and she wouldn't be doing it again.

"Have you ever tried water sports?" It was the next idea supplied by her sub! "Yes, I have. I pissed all over someone while he wanked furiously below me on a hotel floor. It really turned him on, despite it taking me a few attempts for it come out. I got stage-fright," Lou continued. Paul looked surprised but equally aroused. "Would it turn you on to piss in my mouth right now?" "Yes it would," Lou lied. In reality, it wouldn't in the slightest but hey ho, in for a penny, in for a pound and all that.

Remaining straddled across his face, Paul awaited the downstream directly into his eager mouth. Lou relaxed and felt like her urine had begun to escape, but in fact, her body was misleading her. "Are you getting anything there?" she asked. Lou was surprised that he wasn't, so she tried again. Despite the feeling of release, being in this position was just causing her body to freeze! "How about you wee into a cup instead and then make me drink it?" This might be a better arrangement and transpired to be way more successful. Lou stood up, poured the existing drinking water from one glass into another and then placed it between her legs as they chatted. It all seemed a bit random; standing bollock naked in his house, glass strategically positioned between her legs and now filling it with urine rather rapidly as she talked about how easy the flow was now proving! It seemed that this technique was much more effective and there was so much wee; she found herself having to control herself to stop!

Back to where Paul had now sat up, again playing with his cock. She was about to hand him the glass when he said, "Do you want to feed that to me?" 'Well I guess I do,' Lou thought and held it to his lips. He drank a good amount, which was more than she expected. Lou thought he would take a frugal sip, but instead, it was a healthy glug. With that one ticked off, she went to place the glass back on the table. "Don't you want to feed me some more of that?" Well of course she did. It was high on her list of the usual things she did on a normal Saturday afternoon - NOT! Lou held it to his lips once more and he took another hearty drab.

"Do you like my taste?" Lou asked him. "Yes. It tastes like pheromones. Is that the word I'm looking for?" She assumed it was. It sounded about right given he was drinking of her body. "I'm surprised it doesn't taste of gin and tonic from last night or from the two mugs of tea I drank this morning!" Paul smiled. "Actually I can taste the tea!" How funny! "I can freeze the rest in ice cube trays and have one in my drink every day. Would that turn you on?" Again she went with it. "Yes, it would. Take one every day till they run out." Lou had no idea if he would carry this instruction out. They had made many an agreement on the morning after his nights out, but she never knew if he ever kept to his word.

They lay down. Kissing restarted and Paul was giving his member a good yank once more. She wondered how much more his cock and balls would take. Facing each other, he lifted her right knee into his groin. He motioned for her to slam it into him as he masturbated. 'Really?' Lou wondered. He was really going for it, so she applied more and more pressure each time. As Lou built it up, Paul was beginning to groan louder, and she could tell it wouldn't be long before he finally allowed his body to do what it was built to. Rhythmically she plunged her knee into him harder and there it was. Clear water-like come shot passed his shoulder, narrowly missing Lou's face, and onto the cushion behind them, followed by more jets of the same onto his stomach. Lou was surprised at the composition of it. She'd expected it to be creamy and pungent if he hadn't had an orgasm for some time. But who knew what the truth was with him. It didn't matter at this point.

Now it was his turn to laugh. He obviously needed the release and Lou was pleased to have helped him get there. Paul was shocked at the velocity but quite pleased with himself too. He looked like the weight of the world had been lifted from his shoulders and he was alive again. There was a distinctive change in him. He was now blissfully lighter in load (and load ha)! Perhaps that was his first one for a while after all?

A moment later Paul jumped up, cleaned himself off and took the glass away. "I'm starving now. Let me go out and get us some food!" Lou wasn't going to object. She was ravenous too and she had certainly earned it. She was quite happy when he skipped off to go source some nourishment. It allowed her to take a moment to digest the events of the day and process what she felt about it. It had certainly been a different afternoon to what she had expected. It was interesting to reflect on how easily she had become so dominant and how naturally it felt too. Watching his pleasure made her feel good, in whatever shape or form that took, just as pissing on Snake Hips had done many moons before.

Could she go again and have another round with him when he returned? Probably, but it would have to be of the 'vanilla' variety and she wasn't even sure if he was into that. That's just what she fancied after the afternoon's antics. Might he desire that too? She didn't know him well enough to tell. It was a very odd pairing, the two of them, and she was never really sure what it was exactly, other than mutual exploration and sexual enlightenment.

Lou decided she would head back after food. It was a bit of a trek across London and out the other side, but the comforts of her own house and the normality within it (comparatively speaking and all subjective of course), was calling her home and that's just what she needed right now, even if it would take nigh on two hours to get there. Paul was a little disappointed to learn she would not be spending the night, but graciously accepted Lou's decision. They would be in touch again, where their discoveries of dominant and submissive tendencies were sure to continue for them both.

Chapter 12 – Her own personal Jesus

'Well, he's a bit of a dick!' Lou thought to herself as she watched a rather hot man have his partner comb through his sea-soaked, long, brown hair. What a shame! Until then she thought he might have potential.

When she saw him arrive at the beach on his own, she thought he looked attractive with a very different look he clearly owned. It had been years since Lou had seen any man with hair of that style. It was possibly a little longer than her own, which itself draped over her shoulders and beyond. (She had consciously decided to grow it when her daughter suggested it would make her look younger. It was now about the same length it had been when Lou had her first child over twenty years ago.)

He looked Spanish and he had a fit body. Standing around 5' 8", he wasn't overly tall, but he carried himself with purpose, without looking arrogant. His shape wasn't of the over-zealous gym addict, but she could tell he did work out. He was toned and rather pleasing to the eye, and up until that point, she thought she would like to get to know him. But the act of someone else tending to his hair had really turned her off. She couldn't even place why it irritated her so much, but she considered it a weak manoeuvre, almost belittling as well as thoughts of conceitedness. Hey ho - move on!

Lou was having her usual escape to her happy place - Gran Canaria. It was where she loved to enjoy the naturist beach where she shared moments of naked sunbathing, swimming and chatting with people from all over the world in the same attire! There was nothing more liberating and it meant no tan lines either, which was a bonus!

Lou continued her blissful day, stretching out on her towel and basking in the glorious 30C sunshine. As usual, she had travelled there on her own, which meant she could do whatever she wanted (and whoever she wanted) without any compromise. She had no one to please except herself - unless other opportunities presented themselves of course.

Today had begun with Lou deciding to have breakfast at the Cita Centre where her Filipino friend Jocelyn worked. They had made a connection a few of Lou's visits ago and she always made sure she popped in to see her whenever she was on the island. After feeling suitably nourished and with towel already in hand, Lou walked along the avenue that led directly to the Mirador, where the trek across the dunes began to the beach. The sand was heating up, so Lou marched as quickly as possible and soon found herself somewhat parched as she arrived at Kiosk 4.

Lou chose to lay her towel on the sand (having to agree on this with no one else and this was what she liked about holidaying solo), removing the solitary item of clothing she was wearing and then making her way to the bar. The floral strappy dress didn't make much of a pillow for her, but it sufficed.

At the bar, she was greeted by Anthony, who Lou had met a day or so before. He seemed a nice enough chap and it transpired they had seen each other at the very same place two years before, although they had never spoken until this holiday. By the end of the trip, Lou discovered he was a genuine, down to earth, lovely guy who became a good friend.

Anthony offered Lou a drink, and it was while sipping on a shandy there that she spotted this new visitor to the area; one that she had never seen on her previous visits. His friend must have arrived while Lou was sunbathing, as she didn't notice he was with anyone else initially. His companion was a local who Lou didn't recognise either.

After chatting with Anthony, Lou spent some hours of uninterrupted chilling out, which was just how Lou liked it. It wasn't long before something out of the ordinary happened and Lou considered that nothing seemed to surprise her about this place. There was always something to report home about and usually far away from the 'norm'.

With the sun beating down on her oiled skin, it was time to cool down in the refreshing Atlantic Ocean. At this time of the year, the water wasn't quite as bearable as it was in September when Lou would find herself in and out of the water a number of times per day. The water hadn't quite warmed up yet and was likely to give her instant palpitations with the coldness! But Lou was hot and she needed a wee, so she decided to give it a go anyway. To her surprise, the water was pleasantly warmer than anticipated once she got over the initial chilly shock.

The shoreline was busy with similar-minded individuals basking in the glorious weather. Lou had spied a man eyeing her up at the kiosk and had noticed him there earlier in the week too. He was late forties, around six feet tall and slim. He wore a straw hat and was always alone with a trusted book as his accompaniment. Lou felt him look at her once more as she walked past him to the destination of her towel, just a few metres in front. (Lou always had a good perception of people in most scenarios, naked or clothed. It wasn't just her peripheral vision but more of a vibe she picked up. She had a particular penchant for being able to spot a 'player'. She called it her 'Playdar' and he was definitely on it.)

Lou paid him no attention as she submerged herself in the cooling water. It was glorious and there was no better way to swim than stark naked without restrictive clothing. It was so liberating, as her friend Chris had pointed out on her first trip to this lovely paradise.

After around fifteen minutes, Lou decided to return to the shore. While she had been swimming she had noticed the same man staring at her. It was quite obvious as there was no one else around her in the sea. She held his stare, albeit a little way away, and she could see that he was discreetly touching himself below his book. It made Lou smile inside, but she didn't immediately show her reaction.

The water was now shallow enough to stand and deliberately slowly, Lou walked out onto the sand. She saw that the gentle caressing of his penis he previously employed had now turned into a furious yanking. As her body was now fully exposed, he stepped it up even faster. They made eye contact and they both knew exactly what was happening here. Continuing her intentionally sluggish return to her towel, she maintained the stare and grinned. He returned the gesture and as he did so, he forcefully shot his load into his cupped other hand. Lou thought he did well to conceal his excitement to this point, but it was obvious to her what had just transpired. To his credit, this mischievous act had only been theirs to share. It didn't affect anyone else's experience at the beach. They smiled once more and his towel became the chosen tool to wipe up the residual evidence.

Lou returned to her towel and lay down. The sun was again baking her tanned skin and she laughed to herself about what had just happened. In other circumstances this had the makings of a sordid and perverse act, but here it was just another occurrence to add to the crazy experiences Lou encountered. She didn't see it as weird, well not here anyway. Lou was a sucker for attention after all and this naughty shared moment had given them both some pleasure, in different ways. There was no harm done.

At around 5.30pm she noticed this naked sanctuary was emptying out. The wind was a little chilly now and many people had packed up or were preparing to leave. Lou went to put her rubbish in the bin at the kiosk and noticed him sitting there, now alone again. Their eyes met and at that moment Lou could tell instantly that this longhaired, tanned loveliness was radiating happy vibes. Maybe she had read him or the earlier situation incorrectly before. Either way, she felt unable to do anything else but to approach him with a beaming smile back.

"Hola" was all it took and the connection was cemented. His name was Jesus (pronounced 'Ay-Zus'), and he had recently moved to the island from mainland Spain. Around his neck was a leather band with a small copper whale tail hanging from it. Each ear was pierced: the left with three small hoops and the right with one hoop, plus the tragus. He looked ever more the surfer dude as she studied him more closely. They began to chat and it was sparkly eyes and laughter all round. He was certainly easy to speak with and their conversation could have carried on for much longer, but Lou had other commitments. She had already arranged to go shopping after the beach with her new Canarian friend Angi. Lou could not stay long but did manage to exchange numbers with Jesus and they promised to meet up the day after, which just so happened to be Good Friday. Lou wondered what that would have in-store. 'What a strange course of events,' she thought, particularly given her complete about-turn (now about-turns) where Jesus was concerned.

As is quite often the case in the Canaries, the wind can become quite extreme and you find yourself being blasted to the point of sand exfoliation if you stay out in it for any space of time. Lou was hoping it would calm down the next morning when she headed for the beach once more. She had spied the sand being flung across the dunes before she began her descent into them at the start of her journey, but ever hopeful of some calm, she soldiered on to the kiosk.

Once Lou arrived, it was obvious this was not the case. It was blowing up a gale, so she sought refuge on the sun beds. At least there was the windbreak there, although today it was not proving to be too effective as a form of defence. Even still, Lou braved the oncoming attack and stood, or rather laid, her ground. At one point she wrapped her dress around her head and secured it with her hair band so that her left ear would not be continuously filled up with sand. It seemed to do the trick. Lou was very pleased that Jesus would be coming later after work and not before to find her looking this attractive! It wasn't a great look to be fair - not flattering in the slightest!

Over Whatsapp, they agreed to meet at around 14.30 hours, but there had been a traffic accident, so Jesus was running about a half an hour late. It made no difference to Lou. She wasn't going anywhere or perhaps she should be to avoid this continuous wind and sandblasting! Jesus explained that the weather would be much calmer in the dunes away from the 'calima'. 'Oh yeah. Right you are. I know what your game is,' Lou thought. When she declined the offer, he responded with, "We can get comfortable with each other." Lou thought this was somewhat presumptuous and it immediately got her back up. She didn't want to have sex with him in the dunes. She might be tempted somewhere else, but not straight away either. 'Cheeky sod,' she thought.

Apparently there was a translation issue here. Jesus retorted, "No need to freak out. When I say get comfortable, what I mean is that I would like to get to know you more, have some conversation and find out about you. As well as this, it is more sheltered, so you won't be attacked by the wind, or me!" Lou was still in two minds, but it did put her more at ease. "Let's just see what the weather is like when you get here, and we can decide then."

Around twenty minutes later Lou spied Jesus approaching the sun beds. The wind had briefly eased off a few minutes before but was now picking up again. Lou looked up as he greeted her and she was almost ready to leave straight away. There wasn't exactly much to gather up, and fortunately, her dress was no longer strategically placed around her head as the sand-break! After putting it back on properly, Lou bid farewell to the pleasant German man in his sixties with whom she'd spoken a few times and they made their way off. Lou was sure there would be some gossiping starting about them at and around the kiosk as he whisked her away. 'Yeah. Whatever. Long hair, don't care!' Lou thought, coining her daughters' favourite term, as they departed in the direction of the dunes.

Jesus was true to his word and as they walked together across the sand, he found them an area where there was no wind at all, yet it was out in the open at the edge of the bushes. They laid their towels down next to each other and proceeded to de-robe. At that point Lou noticed his shaved body, barring his pubes, which were evident around his cock and balls. She didn't dwell on staring at them, but a quick glance was all it took to notice.

And so the 'getting comfortable' began. It became clear that this was a good term for it after all because it wasn't long before she felt completely at ease with Jesus. She discovered that he was very intelligent and worldly, mainly because he had worked and lived in many countries. He explained how he had been a masseur, potential (but not accepted) gigolo, scuba diving instructor and had also worked filming footage of dives for other people. His current employment saw him shooting choreography promotion and training videos and he would be travelling to London later that week!

Lou felt he was a breath of fresh air. She loved meeting and finding out about new people and the worlds they lived in compared with her own. It was all so very interesting to hear about their experiences and what excited them; what their philosophies and passions were (and not just of the sexual variety).

Lou's estimations of him were way higher now that she had spent some time with him. They increased even more when he brought some chilled beer and pistachio nuts out of his bag. "A picnic!" Lou proclaimed. "How you spoil me." While making a small joke, Lou was flattered by his kindness. How sweet of him. Later he revealed he had three cans of beer, nuts, apples, bananas and a homemade sandwich to share. What a gem and what a result! Lou hadn't realised how hungry she was until this point.

During their time speaking and learning about

each other, a young Spanish-looking man walked past them once, all full of smiles and expectations. He was indicating that he was available, should they want him to join them for sex, but their meeting today was not about rolling around frolicking in the sand. Lou had made that clear, possibly unnecessarily so, but it was certainly understood. Jesus waved him off and respectfully he soon departed.

Another man later walked past them a few times, clearly hoping for a saucy show, but was again treated with the same gesture. There was nothing to see here, although the masturbating meerkats had been known to take pleasure in just watching a naked woman sleeping. Jesus made her chuckle saying the woman could be dead and still they would wank. He was certainly funny and his whole face lit up when he laughed. He was rather gorgeous. Lou knew they would be having sex at some point today. She was finding him hard to resist but maintained her calm, for now, anyway.

Jesus had been sitting up for most of this encounter whilst Lou had mainly been lying on her back catching the rays. For all this time together so far, their conversation took no breaks. It flowed as easily as the beer, accompanied by the nuts. What an excellent combination he had introduced her to.

Mirroring her recent change of position, Jesus decided to lie on his front too and asked if she would apply some factor 50 on his back, to which she obliged. It felt a little odd to start with as she didn't really know him, but she soon got into it, made more hilarious by the sun cream coming out

139

in jets rather than an even spray. She totally missed her intended target a few times, and it shot onto the back of his hand and across the sand, narrowly avoiding his bag too. Fortunately, he couldn't see most of her mishaps, but landing on his palm was a bit of a giveaway! It gave them both another reason to laugh together. To make up for it, she gave him a full body coating in sun protection and she quietly rather enjoyed rubbing cream into his cute bum as well as his legs.

Ever the gentleman (or discreet perv) Jesus offered to do the same in return and Lou happily accepted. In keeping with this approach, he wasn't in any way sexual. It was a purely perfunctory process, which Lou had to admit she was a little disappointed with. It was the right thing to do though, given she had made her expectations clear earlier. He showed respect and that went a long way.

Now both lying on their stomachs side by side, their conversation continued. Lou was secretly thrilled now that she had agreed to spend some time with him. He was fascinating and his general knowledge was impressive too. She found out things about the Foo Fighters she had never known before and other rock paraphernalia. She was hanging on his every revelation and he was teaching her lots, even some English words that she had never heard of, like 'perspicacity'! (*Feel free to go Google that one if you don't know it.*) He was quite inspiring.

By lying so close, it was only natural at some stage that they would find themselves staring into each other's faces. "Your eyes are beautiful and so blue!" Jesus blurted out unexpectedly. Lou thanked him, knowing how much brighter they looked when she had a tan. "I was just going to say how lovely your eyes are too, but obviously not the blue comment." Lou laughed. His eyes were a hazel brown and were glistening as they spoke. It seemed they were lighting each other up and if anyone could have measured their auras, they would have been glowing with happiness. At this stage they had no idea just how this would develop, but it was soon sealed with an exploratory kiss. Jesus leaned in and Lou responded in the same way. Their tongues met and a slow, deep and delicious kiss began.

While Lou enjoyed this moment, she was conscious of their surroundings and was blessed with the knowledge that before long they would undoubtedly be surrounded by masturbating men. She decided to cut the kiss a little short. "I don't want the meerkats to come," Lou explained. He completely understood and smiled as he agreed with her. "Yes, you are right. They appear out of nowhere! We will have to find somewhere more discreet to continue - if that is what you want."

Lou did want, but both felt content to continue basking in the glorious sunshine for a little longer. There was no urgency. They were both very relaxed and savoured the moment. They did steal a few more kisses during the rest of their stay before deciding to pack up and head back.

"Would you like to come to my apartment to get 'de-sanded?" Lou laughed as she said it. "De-sanded?" He asked as if it was an English word he had never heard before. "I may have just made that word up," Lou said, knowing that one wouldn't be found in the English dictionary. Jesus was smiling now too. "I would love to come and get de-sanded with you."

Fortunately his car was parked close to where they exited the dunes, so he was able to get rid of a few items before accompanying her on the short walk along to hers. All the way they didn't stop talking, as seemed the norm for today. They could not get enough of each other, verbally, mentally and soon physically too.

Given her earlier sandblasting experience, Lou decided to take a shower after putting the TV on and finding a suitable channel that would appeal to his rock music preferences. Meanwhile, Jesus opened the bottle of red wine that the apartment owner had kindly left for her. The wine was allowed to breathe as he joined her in the bathroom. Sadly the shower was not big enough for them both to fit in, so he sat in the bathroom chatting whilst she removed the unwanted sand from all those nooks and crannies. Lou liked the fact that he stayed with her. It felt more courteous and displayed his considerate and caring side. It was almost like they both didn't want to miss out on any moment apart.

Given they had both been at the beach naked, there was no awkwardness about getting in or out of the shower in front of each other. Jesus put his hair up in a bun and then got in. Lou returned the compliment of remaining in the bathroom as he 'de-sanded'. She moisturised her sun-kissed skin while still discussing music, language, work, family and just about every other topic available. It was just a shame the shower door had a patterned opaque finish, as she would have loved to have watched him lather himself up. Better still if she could have fit in there with him and done that for him.

Once out and dried, they shared another kiss before moving back into the lounge. Again it was tender and equally thrilling. It was a shame to interrupt this by having to pull out the sofa bed, but it was necessary. As they became more comfortable lying down, songs they had spoken about earlier in the day magically appeared on the TV before them. It was just one coincidence after another, but Lou didn't believe in coincidences, as *Vanilla Extract* readers will know.

The kissing resumed and continued in its delicacy for a while. Jesus's touch was light; stroking her arms and neck as they lay side by side. His skin was soft, and she nuzzled into him. Lou was enjoying this slow, sensual approach and it wasn't long before her stomach started to flinch as he caressed her. Lou's nipples were erect throughout. She had no control over them, but soon he did. He was drawn to them, taking one in each hand and squeezing them. Immediately currents were sent to her clitoris and the moistness began to build.

Jesus had been nothing but kind to her. Now she wanted to give something back, so she began to kiss his neck and then down to his defined chest. Dragging her tongue across his nipples, Lou gauged whether he was sensitive there. She had found that some men's nipples were completely unaffected by her touch (or females for that matter), while others were driven wild by their tweaking and nibbling. Without much response, she continued her journey downwards, where she found his swollen member ready for her. Lou would tease him first before beginning the devouring.

Lou was pleased to find him watching her as she licked his inner thighs and groin area. The anticipation was growing in his eyes as she toyed with her tongue strokes before taking him in her mouth. His penis was a good size; not too much girth, not too long and it fit perfectly in her mouth as she built up to deep-throating him. The silky saliva produced was excellent for sliding her hand up and down his shaft ever so gently, with or without her awaiting mouth at the top. Now he was relaxing more into it. His body was telling her he was feeling a whole lot more comfortable as he began to make accompanying noises with his moves and twitches. She heard the odd sigh of delight and encouraging hip movement as she tried new things out on him. 'Mmmm' all round as Lou found herself also getting excited by his reactions.

Lou had learned that there are times when delivering a blowjob that the giver can feel a rush of fluid upwards from the base of the cock. It doesn't usually end with ejaculation, but it normally indicates it's definitely getting closer. A few of these and the receiver may panic as they are losing control. This is where Lou would then calm her motions down and let things settle, by going back to light tongue caressing and kissing around the area. Alternatively Lou would move back to the mouth and concentrate on kissing to aid distraction.

CINNAMON TWIST

It was after a couple of these rushes that Jesus said he wanted to lick her. They had discussed song lyrics earlier in the day, particularly oral pleasure and how one singer who hated the taste. Lou said he obviously hadn't tried her! She had received no complaints! Now it was Jesus's turn to prove her theory, as he told her to lie down so he could begin. Lou did so quite happily as the anticipation had been growing steadily for some time now.

And there it was: his soft tongue gliding on her clit. It was heaven! Just what she wanted after such a long wait. It slid ever so delicately from side to side and then deep inside. OMG, that felt good. Ooh yeah; he was great at that. There was nothing quite as exciting for her than kissing someone for the first time (if they were a good kisser of course) and then discovering the newfound oral skills of a stranger - especially one as hot as Jesus.

It was a first for her to look down and see a long-haired man nourishing himself on her juices. He definitely had a thirst and Lou soon found herself wriggling around on the bed. His arms firmly kept her in place as her stomach began to somersault with his every stroke. She so wanted him to be inside her. How long would he pleasure her before introducing his lovely cock to her inner sanctum? She hoped it would be soon. Instead, a finger slipped in and added to her sensitivity. However good the tongue was, sliding a finger or two in at the same time always intensified the sensation. 'Hell yes, here we go!' Lou thought to herself.

Lou's own anticipation was leading the way

145

now and his expert skills soon had her sucking in air as she shrieked with delight. Was he going to make her come just with oral? Her rhythmic breathing deepened to more of a pant and there it was, completely out of her control, her orgasm escaped and possibly along with a small squirt too, although she found it hard to tell. "Fuck, fuck, fuck!" Lou shouted as she drew Jesus tight into her chest and held him there for a while. She was in shock and a little embarrassed at her outburst, but now feeling as light as a feather. She decided to cling on to him until her body returned to its pre-euphoric state.

It took a few moments for Lou to breathe normally again. When she released him from her grip, Jesus said, "That was so hot!" He was right too. What a horny start to their session and this could only get better!

Jesus grabbed a condom and put in on while Lou regained her composure. She was super excited, still tingling and couldn't wait to finally feel him inside her. Lou hoped she wouldn't be disappointed. She doubted she would be. He had a lovely cock and given his now-proven skills; this should be delightful indeed.

'Jesus in the missionary position!' It was a little ironic but made Lou smile. She would keep that one to herself. Looking down at her with those beautiful eyes, he entered her slowly. Lou couldn't help but let out a light gasp as they tenderly became one.

Locked in a stare, he held himself there for a short while before it all went a little crazy. Fuelled by the rock music in the background, the amazing connection and the passion, a full-on fuck fest continued to all new heights! Pounding in time with Aerosmith, Blur and the Rolling Stones, Jesus and Lou were enjoying the ultimate physical act while laughing, singing and generally being silly!

A change in tempo meant a change in position and soon Lou was straddling him and riding on top. Now it was her turn to look down at him. Jesus was smiling up at her with those sparkly eyes. She grabbed his chest as she dug down with her hips. He responded immediately and pushed upwards. "Ooh yeah, that's even deeper," Lou said as they both forced their bodies still tighter together.

Oh, this was fun. It had been a while since Lou had enjoyed a first encounter so much. Time was flying and they had no idea what hour it was. They were lost in this delicious, messy moment that was getting better and better.

Lou loved this position. She was able to control exactly what went on. If she wanted it more intense, she could speed up her motions. Once done with that, Lou could go up onto her feet and squat up and down or spin around for some reverse cowgirl. There were many choices on offer here; all divine in their different ways.

When the Foo Fighters came on, Jesus swept her up, and Lou found herself now lying back on the bed again. Above her, Lou couldn't tell if his fingers inside her made her gush or whether he was wanking himself vigorously into her. Either way, the forceful internal rubbing turned the waterworks on almost instantly (but not the urine kind). The damp patch on the sofa bed beneath them spread very quickly and it wasn't easing off, well not until he stopped her stream.

Jesus's next move was to fuck her hard. The time was right. They had explored each other enough a few times in various positions and Lou thought he deserved to come too. As good as this was, Jesus had certainly earned it. Lou moved down the bed as he lied on his side. He removed the condom and she took his penis in her mouth. Oddly it didn't taste rubbery, despite the friction it had been through. Jesus was moaning with her sucking and she knew he was close but wasn't sure exactly where he would come. She wanked him into her mouth, but it wouldn't be ending there. (This didn't meet her 'privileged access' criteria and it was hardly sexually safe either.)

Just as Jesus was about to come, Lou pulled his cock into her chest and that was where he deposited his load. His heavenly groans filled the room Lou felt the warm wet liquid cover her neck and chest as it shot out. It then dribbled down her skin and some onto the sofa bed. "You've given me a pearl necklace!" Lou declared, but it was a term Jesus was unfamiliar with. Perhaps that one didn't translate, well not until after she explained and he saw the funny side.

They held each other close for a while and laughed about the crazy sex session they had just shared. Some red wine sips followed the cleanup and it wasn't very long at all before Lou experienced Jesus's second coming and then third in the morning. A total of eight hours had been spent 'getting comfortable' as such, in her apartment. They had sex for more hours than they had slept and at this rate Lou would have a whole new jewellery collection – of the pearl variety!

Lou spent the next day mainly drifting in and out of sleep at the beach. She hoped her clit wasn't looking like a beacon, as there was no hiding it on a nudist beach. Fortunately it was not too swollen and the seawater and sunshine helped! It was just a shame she would have to wait until the following day to see Jesus, which just so happened to be Easter Sunday. Lou did not doubt at all that he would be rising again.

Chapter 13 – Steamy Sydney

Working in the same team made any public shows of affection a little tricky, but Lou and Ross had managed to keep their relationship under wraps for a few months now. They had the same boss but worked in different offices. This was probably a good thing or else they'd never get any work done. They already found each other quite a distraction, even from afar.

Their liaisons started as a result of their boss actually. Unbeknown to them both, there was a mutual attraction going on which was brought to life when their boss mentioned Lou's seamed stockings being rather 'racy', to which they all laughed. "I like to feel good in the office," she had retorted. It was just the three of them in a meeting room in London where the comment was made. Ross was down for the day from Manchester, and their meeting was now finished. As always, it was quite a light-hearted meeting, still getting the work completed, but with a jovial manner about them.

By the time Lou had returned to her desk, he had instant messaged her on the work systems. "Great set of pins inside those stockings, lass." And that was how it had all begun. A year of saucy and very naughty encounters was to follow, with each pushing her boundaries a little further. The secrecy in the workplace made it all the more exciting and the connection was very real. In that time they knew exactly how the other one ticked and also what turned each other on. It was a shared mission to maximise every moment they shared.

A business trip to Sydney proved to be a very exciting adventure. Ross was attending a conference the week before and Lou would be joining in his second week, along with some of their other team members. Their carefully constructed and rather naughty plan had been to take it in turns to leave envelopes for each other on reception with instructions contained within. No details would be revealed in advance, but the goal was to make each session a different fantasy.

Given that Lou was arriving second, Ross would leave the first envelope. Lou's anticipation on the business class flight was growing by the hour. She hoped she wouldn't be jet lagged or too exhausted to carry out whatever the contents contained. Ross had also given her instructions to read 'The Story of O' on the way, which she had completed. (Lou found it exciting to start but felt it lost its way after a while. All the same, it was a good read and got her in the mood on route!)

Lou's taxi dropped her at the Sheraton. She noticed a few fellow colleagues from other teams out having a smoke as she pulled in. A few 'hello's and poor renditions of 'good day mate' from them and she was in the door and checking in, all the time wondering what he'd left for her welcome.

Once the formalities were completed, Lou asked if there was anything on reception for her. The receptionist had a look under the counter, and sure enough, there was a sealed envelope in her name. Lou recognised her employer's internal mail printed envelope and Ross's writing upon it. It was much fatter than she'd expected. There was obviously something else in there other than written instructions. 'How exciting,' she thought. 'I wonder what it is?'

The weariness of her long flight had taken its toll, even with the luxuriousness of the business class she was unaccustomed to outside of her employer. As comfortable as it was, she was still feeling a little drained, having travelled halfway across the globe! However, the receipt of the package with unknown contents suddenly gave Lou a new bout of energy. She was chomping at the bit and couldn't wait to get to her room to rip it open.

Lou's attention was not on the plush interior of the room that would become her home for the next four nights. A quick glance around the room was all she took in: two kingsize beds, full length curtained windows, a desk at an angle in the corner and an area for her suitcase to be stored next to the wardrobes. She swiftly dumped her case as she rushed to the bed to immediately fall upon it and opened the envelope. As she carefully tore the top, she gazed inside and was surprised to find two envelopes, clearly marked. 'Open this first,' was the one she took out and immediately complied. It was A5 size and flat. Lou was certain it would contain a note, and she was right.

"Welcome to Sydney, you sexy bitch. I will have the pleasure of you soon, but first you need to

do something. Take one of the plain envelopes from the desk in your room and make your way to reception. Ask for a duplicate room key and then write my name and your room number on the envelope. Seal it up and then ask the receptionist to hold it for me there. You may then return to your room and open the second package.

Do it now. The longer you leave it, the longer it will take for me to have you!

Ross X"

The adrenaline, exhaustion, desire and excitement suddenly consumed her body, to the point where Lou couldn't think straight. "Fuck, fuck Lou, get a grip," she reminded herself aloud to her reflection in the mirror as she had a quick wee before going back downstairs. The flesh was certainly willing, but her brain wasn't quite sure!

Eagerly Lou left her hotel room and headed for the lift, fortunately not bumping into anyone else she knew. Discreetly she followed Ross's instructions and was soon back upstairs and ripping open the second envelope. This was more intriguing as she knew it was some form of material inside. To her surprise, Lou found a lace body stocking dress inside, a suspender belt, stockings and a blindfold. (He knew she would bring her high heels, as that was the norm.) What she did notice were missing were any knickers, which amused her. 'Typical Ross,' she thought.

As she laid the garments on her nearest massive bed, she saw a hand-written note inside which read:

'Time for things to get interesting. After your shower I want you to put the lingerie on and your

killer heels. Stand at the desk with your back to the door. Your legs will be shoulder-width apart.

When you are ready, you must message me, then put your phone down on the desk. Place the blindfold over your eyes and your hands on the desk at the same distance apart as your feet.

Wait for me. Do NOT turn around at all.

I shall be inside you soon.

Ross X "

'Holy fuck!' Lou thought. That's super fucking horny. She made her way to the shower and washed away the grubbiness of the plane journey and prepared herself for him. The cleansing waters certainly helped her freshen up and focus. Next was the moisturiser liberally spread from head to toe and now she was feeling much better, all the time psyching herself up for this encounter.

Lou applied her minimal makeup: mascara. That was all she needed to make herself look a little more awake. Extending her lashes brought out the blueness of her eyes, although she felt they were a little pink from the travelling. She doubted he would notice anyway, so why was she bothered? It would be fine. She combed through her wet hair and left it to dry naturally. Brushing her teeth was a tingly sensation and instantly she felt sparkling. It's amazing how stale your mouth can become too when you travel.

'Why the hell do stockings get even more fiddly when you're under pressure?' Lou asked herself. Bloody things - no wonder she preferred hold-ups. They gave almost the same effect without the faffing of trying to get them in place, then securely fastened and looking sexy. No matter, it was what he wanted and she was keen to please him. He'd clearly thought this through before he left England and gone to considerable effort. The stockings were from a UK supplier she noticed, so he had brought it all with him.

Next it was time to put on the dress. That was easy enough as it slipped over her head, but her rings got caught in the mesh and she very nearly tore a new hole in it. Carefully she untangled her hands and pulled it down slowly. Phew! That was lucky!

It was now in place and she was ready for the shoes. Damn it! She should have got them out of the case beforehand, but fortunately, she knew exactly where they were in her sealed suitcase. She went straight to them and they were soon upon her feet. Thank goodness she packed the closed toe ones. Stockings and peep toe were just wrong, in her eyes anyway. That would be a fashion *faux pas,* although not every female shared her thoughts on this style.

Lou was ready, or so she thought. Maybe another quick wee just in case, swiftly freshened up with a wet flannel to make sure she was clean. Now she really was fully prepared or as much as she was going to be. She made her way to the desk and stood as he had requested. Her feet were a shoulder apart and she looked down a few times to check. It had to be perfect, or maybe she was over-thinking? She picked up her phone and messaged him. "I'm ready for you now." 'Fuck, fuck, this is real now' Lou thought. She put the phone down and placed the blindfold over her eyes. The level of adrenaline shot through the roof now and she could feel that her pussy was getting moist. OMG this was really turning her on. It was the build-up: the expectancy. It was overwhelming and all consuming.

A moment of panic set in as Lou suddenly considered her mascara and the blindfold now squashing her eyes. 'Damn. Has she given it enough time to dry properly beforehand? Would she look like panda eyes when he finally removed it?' Lou dashed to the bathroom. 'Shit! Shit! Shit!' He'd best not arrive now!

Her fears were allayed when she checked her eyes. They were fine. There had been no need to worry. Lou ran back to the desk and resumed the position. She secretly hoped he would be a while so she could calm down, which fortunately he was.

Ross seemed to take bloody ages, as Lou stood with her back to the door, all the while wondering what to expect, with her arousal building rapidly. The anticipation was killing her and she was supercharged. She could feel her juices flowing and she was sure the tops of her thighs were getting wet. Could that be possible? She wanted to look down to check, but she didn't want to be busying herself in case Ross opened the door at that exact moment.

And there it was: the click of a door key being granted access and then the door opening. Lou wanted to scream with excitement, but she couldn't. She also wanted to turn and run up to him, hug him, but she couldn't. The door closed behind him and he was in the room and making his way towards her (or at least Lou hoped it was he. That could have

CINNAMON TWIST

all gone horribly wrong).

His footsteps were light on the thick shagpile carpet as he drew closer. What did he have in mind for her? How was this going to play out? How would this start? Would he bend her over the desk and fuck her senseless or would he take his time and tease her? So many questions were racing through Lou's mind. She just wanted him to do something, anything to take her out of this turmoil, but it was only made worse by the sound of a zip opening. But it wasn't his trousers. He had brought a bag and was now allowing himself access to whatever on earth was inside it.

Lou knew her breathing had grown heavier. She could hear her heart beating loudly in her ears. She gasped as he swept her hair over one shoulder so he could access her neck. There he placed a soft kiss and told her she had been a good girl for following his instructions. "You shall have the greatest of rewards Lou." Tingles darted all over her body. She couldn't exactly tell where but it felt amazing. His hot words were lingering on her neck and with that, he withdrew from her.

Ross stood for a while behind her before continuing. She could feel his presence, but he wasn't moving. He may have been considering what to do next, or he may have been intentionally causing havoc with her brain and body. 'Very likely the latter' Lou thought. Something was on her leg now. It felt hard but his pressure of it was soft. It may have been a crop or a whip handle. It was hard for her to tell. It was applied to her inner side of her left knee. "A little wider," he directed and Lou

157

opened her legs a little further. Holy shit, this was horny. And there she waited. He was deliberately taking his time with every move as Lou wondered where the hell he would be next.

It started at her left ankle. The same tool was now dragging its way up her inner calf and up to her thigh. The touch was light enough to make her stomach quiver and her clit to grow. What the fuck was going on here? Her senses were so heightened that Lou thought she would burst. Then it stopped. 'Damn, damn, damn.' Next was her right leg, with the same tantalising motion. Again, Ross stopped and waited.

Something soft was now caressing both of Lou's legs at the same time. It was tickly and enjoyable at the same time. Ross made his way slowly up them both and didn't stop until they finally made it to her bottom. There he used both feather ticklers across her buttocks and hips. Well that was a new sensation and a very pleasant one too. Ross continued up her back and swirled them around on the exposed skin. Lou could feel shivers not only all up her spine but also pretty much all over her body. She wanted to scream out in delight but wasn't sure if that was the right thing to do. What was the right thing to do exactly? Instead a murmur of pleasure escaped her lips. She couldn't help it. "Aaaaah!" So good!

Once more Ross left her for a moment. She calmed down a little, but still the anticipation was brimming to overflowing. Replacing the feather sensation was one she was more familiar with. It was his tongue and it was sweeping up from her left ankle up her calf and to her thigh. There he lingered a little longer on the outer side before moving into the centre. "I can taste you, Lou. It appears you have been dribbling and your sweet juice is now all over my tongue." OMG, she was right. She was leaking! In normal circumstances she would probably be quite embarrassed, but not now. She said nothing, but some peculiar sound did come out. Lou wasn't sure where it came from. It was more of a moan.

Across to her right thigh and Ross continued the lapping up. He skipped past her wanton pussy as he did so. How she yearned for him to plunge his tongue inside her – maybe a few fingers too. She was certainly ready for him. Instead the strokes of his tongue cleaned her leg and he made his way down the right side too and then paused.

In Lou's mind all she could think of was 'For fuck sake get inside me now', but for whatever reason, she felt she couldn't say it out loud and so kept it locked inside. Waiting, wanting, hoping for more contact, preferably of the internal type, she listened for clues as to what would be next. Her senses were on full alert and she was surprised to find it was her smell that was activated next. From inside the bag Ross pulled out a rose. The scent was distinctive as he rolled it over her bottom and then brought it round to her front where it caressed her breasts. (Even in this state of excitement, Lou's practical head jumped into play. She wondered if he had removed the thorns, which of course he would have, but she couldn't help but think of it!)

The petals were incredibly soft as they swept

ever so lightly over her skin. Who knew you could find so much pleasure from a flower other than the usual, more traditional visual or fragrant way? Lou only hoped he wasn't going to put it anywhere near her nether regions as it would certainly be destroyed with all the moisture! She was quite pleased when it was cast aside. It had been ok, but nothing to write home about. Next!

Back to audio stimulation now in the form of another zip being unfastened. This time it was his trousers. (A silent 'yippee' was triggered in Lou's mind.) They didn't fall to the ground in a heap or thrown across the room. Meticulously he folded his trousers and hung them over the nearby chair. He must have slipped his shoes off without her knowing because now he was hopping around removing his socks in a somewhat less organised fashion! (But she was glad they were off. There was nothing less sexy than keeping socks on!)

Lou heard his shirt being unbuttoned and that too was then placed on the chair. Well there was no point in getting anything creased up. Ross would probably be wearing that ensemble tomorrow when he joined their other work colleagues for the rest of the offsite. Meanwhile Lou was bursting in anticipation. How long would it be until he was finally inside her?

Reaching across to his bag once more, she heard Ross take a box of what she assumed was condoms , ripped open the cellophane top and then placed them on the desk so she could see them. He certainly was prepared.

It seemed to Lou that he purposefully unzipped

his trousers as slowly as humanly possible: as if every notch was pulled at tortoise speed. She heard every click. Maybe it was because of her erupting desire, but with heightened senses, she thought she was losing control of her usual demeanour. How had he done this to her? It felt like time had slowed down at that point. Was this normal under such circumstances or was this way off the scale? How could she ever know until perhaps after the event when they discussed just how it had gone for them both? Maybe they could have a post-implementation review (PIR)? She wasn't even sure if this was completely new for him or he'd played this part before. He certainly seemed to know what he was doing. Again this would be up for discussion post-coital. Time now to relax and enjoy whatever pleasures were next and she was certain he would totally tease and tantalise her even more. She was not disappointed.

Ross's hands now touched her back. It seemed like forever since she had felt his skin on hers. They were clammy and she felt the moisture in them as they caressed her back. It wasn't long before they were holding her hips as he drew closer to her. Lou couldn't help but sigh. Damn, she was horny - to the point of bursting if he didn't get inside her soon. Briefly letting her go, Ross reached to the desk and drew a condom out of the packet. Opened and on, he needed no additional lubrication to guide himself in. Lou was certainly ready for him. She had been for a very long time it seemed. A moment later and she felt his throbbing cock on her labia. It was time – thank fuck! He was finally going to seduce her. Savouring every tingle, he continued to slide until he was fully engulfed in Lou's body. Ross let out a groan. It was the first time she had heard anything from him since he let himself in her room and it was pure, animalistic pleasure. Meanwhile Lou was a whimpering mess, audibly and physically, but in a totally good way!

"Holy shit Ross. That's fucking amazing!" And it was. Whether it was the build-up, the deprivation or whatever it was, it had sent them both wild. Taking their time was now over. It was time to unleash their inner beasts and that's when it got just a little bit crazy. Ross bent her over the desk fully, forcing her head down onto the surface; face planted on her left cheek and fucked her hard, pausing only to spread her legs wider. Screams of delight filled the room and neither of them cared who heard. It was too rampant for that. There was only one mission in both their minds and that was fulfilling their carnal desires by getting as deep as was physically possible into each other. Ross pounded her as hard as he possibly could and Lou absolutely loved it. It was just what the doctor ordered after all that teasing.

Ross span her around and lifted her up onto the desk. He removed the blindfold and placed a delicate kiss on her lips before he filled her mouth with his tongue. 'Damn, this is so hot' Lou thought. Straddled and soaked, she took his member deep again. He was like a machine and his continuous pumping made both her and the desk move across the floor only to collide with the wall. They both laughed as it then banged against the wall continuously. Perhaps it was time to relocate before next door complained?

"Your bathroom should have the same mirror as mine. I've been fantasising about watching me fuck you against the sink since I arrived last week." Instantly they gathered themselves up and headed for it, with no further words spoken. Ross knew Lou loved watching as much as he did, so there were certainly no complaints from her.

Switching the main light on as they entered, Lou assumed the doggy position at the basin. He was right. The mirror was enormous and the lighting was perfect. She watched as he lined himself up, grabbed onto her and forced his dribbling penis back inside. "Oh fuck that's good!" He blurted out. "That's it: deep inside your beautiful pussy. I've waited for fucking ages to be inside you, Lou!" She concurred. It had felt like he'd been away for a very long time, when in fact it was only two weeks since she'd last seen him in London. They were certainly making up for lost time now.

The continuous knocking against her cervix was feeling a little uncomfortable now, but the over-riding pleasure was compensating, as was watching this glorious scene unfold in their reflection. It was bloody sexy to watch. Lou studied Ross's facial expressions as he adjusted his footing and the stance from which he probed. He stared at her biting her lip as new internal sensations were explored and enjoyed.

Mixing it up a little more, Lou raised her right leg and placed her foot on the bath edge. It allowed easier access (not that it was needed but it provided a different angle). Her stiletto was placed on the bath rim and gave her a little support, but not much. In the mirror they both looked in awe at his juice-drenched cock sliding in and out. The moisture was all over his groin area too. She had saturated him and a small puddle was beginning to form below them. "Someone's pleased to see me," Ross said as he looked down at the creamy residue covering the condom's exterior.

Ross laughed and then decided it was time for some real wetness to be made. Withdrawing his sodden member from her, he placed two fingers up inside Lou and began to vigorously pump her vagina. (She had actually brought gushing to his attention before this trip when she recounted her Snake Hips experience with him. Ross had obviously done his homework since then.) It didn't take long at all before the clear liquid was pouring down her leg and onto the floor. Ross was looking incredibly pleased with himself. "Looks like you've got that one mastered Ross." Lou applauded. A continuous stream was flowing with every finger thrust. He had certainly turned the taps on, which was fitting given where they were.

Lou kicked off her both her shoes; one rather more sodden than the other, reminding her of that early gushing memory and looked around the room for the next location to fuck. Ross knew she was scoping the facilities. "How about on the bath edge?" Lou backed herself against it and placed her hands on the back against the wall. Her legs were dangling over the edge nearest him and soon they were one again. However, this wasn't particularly

164

comfortable for either of them, so that was soon abandoned.

Lou decided to give him some oral pleasure instead. He had done most of the work so far, so it was only fair. Lou lowered herself to the floor and on her knees before him, she removed the condom. "I think you've earned this," she said as she guided his cock into her mouth and began to suck him off slowly. Now it was his turn to gasp. "Fuck Lou, that's perfect." She took her time. She wanted to let things settle a bit before turning the frantic meter up a notch again.

Lou devoured him carefully, wanting him to feel every lick, nibble and kiss. Tonight he had stimulated her senses as they had never been before. (Well that's how it felt at the time. Whether this really was the first time she'd felt this, she would question later, but for now, it was like her intensity cherry was being popped all over again!) Back to Ross and savouring him with intent. Lou enjoyed looking at his side reflection as well as his face, as she went up and down his shaft, then bringing her saliva-covered hand into play intermittently and wanking him in between movements.

"Lou you're gonna have to stop that or I'll come in your mouth." Lou contemplated that and decided that she wouldn't mind if he did. He was one of the very few who had earned her 'privileged access', and this was within that category. (*Vanilla Extract readers will know that Lou's 'privileged access' is only granted to people who have earned her respect and are within her circle of trusted regulars.*)

Whilst Lou didn't necessarily want this scenario to end, she was tired, it had been a long day and she doubted this encounter would get any better than it already had. With that in mind, she went to work properly! Her sole desire was to make him come. Her right hand wandered around to his bum and she caressed it before starting on his balls. Ross relaxed into her rhythm. He knew what she was doing here. "Oh, ok," he said as he looked down at her smiling up at him. "As long as you're sure." Lou smiled again and her eyes indicated that was exactly what she wanted. She gripped his cock harder and applied more pressure. "Oh god Lou, I'm so close." And he wasn't lying. Less than a minute later, she felt his body tense up as he cried out, "Fuck Lou, I'm coming!" Lou didn't need the alert. It was already evident as the hot, salty fluid filled her mouth. It was thick too. He must have been saving that up for her. Rather than let it linger, Lou gulped it down, swallowing as fast as she could. Lou was never particularly fond of the flavour, but she knew how much it turned him on, plus, not that they needed it here, it also helped with post-sex clean up. Like a magic trick: 'ta-da, all gone!'

With his flinching penis still in her mouth, Lou held on to his buttocks, pulling them into her face. She felt every shudder until Ross calmed down. He looked down, always surprised and appreciative of her swallowing his sperm. She knew it turned him on and his face was full of glee. "Naughty Lou," he remarked. "Well you know babes. I aim to please," she responded. "Well, you certainly did that all right!"

Throwing the floor towel down, it was immediately wet from their earlier exploits, but now it was to be used for the shower. They both got in together and washed away all traces of their steamy session, then retired to the bed. It was the first time she had felt how comfortable it was since arriving and she knew she would sleep like a log after the day (and night) she had experienced. Ross decided to stay with her, knowing he would have to depart her room super early in the morning to avoid any unwanted bumping into any of their colleagues. She was pleased with the naked cuddling until he snoozed off before her, then she moved away from him. Sexy as he was, she still needed her space for a proper night's sleep.

And so their business trip continued. Lou only hoped Ross would enjoy what she had in store for him the following night. It involved a toy that Lou described to customs as a 'massager' when asked. She was sure he would approve of this bad boy, given that she had also brought the accompanying lubricant. You see, Lou could be very organised too, when she wanted to be.

Chapter 14 – The second coming

Lou always did love an adventure. It took her all over the UK and to other countries too, either partying with good friends in new places or meeting men she had slept with before. (Obviously this did not include revisiting anyone who she had anything less than exceptional sex with. That was now well and truly off her radar.) So when she was invited back to Gran Canaria by his holiness, who was she to refuse?

It was just over a month since they had seen each other for that first heated session at her apartment and now as she walked out of the airport, Jesus was waiting for her, leaning up against his car, with his long hair blowing in the wind and his rugged face full of joy. The greatest of hugs were exchanged before he took her small bag and placed it in the car. This all felt very natural. How soon they had slipped back into place like they'd known each other for years. Neither of them was nervous or awkward, which made the time together very easy indeed. Jesus knew Lou wasn't of the high maintenance variety of women in the slightest and he was super chilled, so this was sure to make for a very smooth and carefree cohabitation.

A quick stop off at the supermarket where they walked hand in hand up the aisles and picked up some provisions that they would later only consume a fraction of. It was then back to the car and off to his place, where the frivolities really began.

Lou was respectful of his apartment after they ascended the three flights of stairs, past the redundant lift. (Fortunately her main cardio exercise was the stepper, so she wasn't out of breath when she got to the top. Jesus was obviously used to it.) She placed her bag on his sofa as he began to unpack the shopping. Lou wasn't sure if she should just jump him there and then, snog his face and rip his clothes off, but she knew there were perishables in the bags. Get some control woman!

Once sorted, Jesus gave Lou a tour of his pad and then offered her a drink, but that was the last thing she wanted and he felt the same as she soon discovered. Jesus leant into her for a kiss as he placed both hands either side of her face and pulled her in close to him. Lou instantly responded internally by becoming a tingling mess. Externally her hands went straight to up his back inside his t-shirt to his shoulder blades and drew him in. A passionate kiss ensued and they were soon lapping at each other with such gusto that Jesus took her hand and dragged her back to his bedroom.

Lou lifted her navy spaghetti vest top over her head and placed it on the cupboard. Down to her bra, she began to remove her brightly coloured flowing skirt, which was next to come off as she pulled it down and stepped out of it. "There you are, Lou. I've missed that body," Jesus said. She smiled and returned to kissing him passionately. He had taken off his top and was starting to unbutton his jeans. Lou nodded in approval. He did have a very good chest, arms, shoulders and more. She was pleased to be reacquainted with his body.

Jesus was now out of his trousers and Lou kicked off her sandals. She was standing in her matching navy two-set. Jesus moved to take up position behind and swept her hair back across her shoulder, so he had easy access to her collarbone and neck. That's where he began to nibble and place delicate kisses all over this area. It was soft and sensual and it was driving her mad. Lou loved it and wanted so much more.

Jesus turned her around so they were facing each other and motioned for her to get comfortable on the bed behind them. "Sit down Lou. I want a taste." 'Fuck!' Lou thought. What a good job she'd had a quick freshen up in the airport toilets as she landed. She had purposely cleaned her 'fandango' with some fresh water following her arrival wee! Always good to be prepared! 'Well you just never know, do you?'

Lou backed herself onto the bed as instructed. She would relish this moment. Jesus soon joined her, but carefully slipped her knickers down both hips before burying his head in her special place. 'Damn that's hot,' Lou thought, loving every moment. She could feel the temperature rising down there, particularly as he parted her labia and slid his flickering tongue inside. Lou had forgotten just how good he was at oral and how long he liked to spend giving it to her. This was perfect as far as she was concerned. This was the best welcome ever!

Lou lost count of the number of times she came.

CINNAMON TWIST

It was a mixture too of smaller waves of euphoria, the continuous 'tap' type of drip feed coming and the crescendo fanfare trumpets style too. Jesus really did have it all going on. Her body was in shock when he finally slipped his throbbing cock inside her and gave her a jolly good seeing to. 'Yum, yum. How good does that feel?" Lou thought to herself as he turned her over and fucked her from behind. Wowza! He could have gone on and on too, but he did have some work to do at some stage, plus they did have the next few days to continue this interlocking. She told him to come all over her arse. "And what a cute little arse it is too Lou. I'll happily cover it for you!" And that was exactly what he did – the first time.

After some work was completed on his videography edits, he was all hers again for the rest of the evening. The Mexican restaurant he wanted to take her to was unexpectedly closed, so they wandered back, and he prepared food in his apartment. It was a good choice too as he had picked up dried meats and presented her with a selection of those, cheese, bread and tomatoes. It was all washed down with a very nice Crianza wine as they chose different songs to play to each other on Spotify at the bar in his kitchen. After a few hours passed, they found themselves back in his bed for more rounds of deliciousness that they craved so badly!

As usual Lou was awake first and found Jesus next to her quietly sleeping. Despite the copious amounts of sex they had shared the evening before, Lou wanted more. It was the norm with her. The more sex she experienced, the more she wanted. It was addictive. She wondered if he would feel the same way, with a little persuasion perhaps?

He was lying on his back to her right. She began by reaching across his body to his ribs and began to caress his side. Gradually she worked her hand down past his waist to his thigh and delicately drew her hand across it. His breathing had changed during the process and she could sense him beginning to stir. Lou then slipped her hand under the cover and was surprised to find his member already awake, even when he appeared not to be so. A few light strokes and she decided it was time to investigate further with her tongue.

Fully submerged in Jesus's bedding, his solid penis was soon inside her mouth. Damn, he felt good. He had got up during the night and gone for a wee, so Lou was hoping he wouldn't have to interrupt this moment with a loo visit. Fortunately this was not the case and he was more than ready for her. "Oh, Lou. What a beautiful way to wake up. I was dreaming that I was in a swimming pool and my cock was getting wet. But this is so so much better." Lou laughed and with her mouth full said, "Well a very good morning to you too," to which he moaned in delight. It was intentionally garbled, but he got the gist!

Lou continued with her breakfast for quite some time before they mixed it up a little. Her jaw was aching slightly, even after she turned him over from his back to his side to allow her better access. It probably had something to do with the hours of oral and fucking last night and the day before that had caused it, but her mouth did feel tired.

After letting him fall out of her, she crept back up the bed and gave him a very deep kiss, which he reciprocated in the same way. The passion between these two was electric. There was no fear of morning breath. They just went straight in for the kill with their lashing tongues and need for every last piece of each other.

Smiling intently at her, his brown eyes were sparkling and he had a very cheeky look in them. It was his turn to crawl down the bed and give her some internal attention and he certainly meant business. In fact, he didn't come up for air, so to speak, for some forty-five minutes, during which time Lou came and gushed and came and gushed again. She lost count (again). He was relentless. Every moment she thought she could take no more, he built her up and let her go again. It started with him licking her labia and clit, with fingers inside her vagina and another rimming her anus. Unusually it was turning her on to levels she'd not experienced for a very long time, well since Lars really. 'Early days on the privileged access,' Lou thought, but she'd make an exception. It felt too good not to. Her orgasm from this combination was strong and deep. It also went on for quite some time, followed almost instantly with furious clit rubbing and another explosion straight afterwards. This was certainly a serious morning session and she was enjoying every tingle of it!

Their bodies felt spent! They would end up killing each other at this rate if they stayed in bed any longer. They decided to get up and go to the beach and let the sunshine and salty water cure their throbbing genitalia! It worked too! They spent the day in the sun on her favourite beach where they pretty much chatted the entire day through. It was brilliant. They had cobbled together a packed lunch, much the same as when he had first entertained her at the beach a month or so ago. What a bloody shame he had to fly off to Budapest a day later for work and their adventure was to be cut short. Next time she would have to have him for longer, although she did wonder if her bits could take it! Mmmm, what a dilemma – NOT!

Lou spent two further days at his apartment during which time she felt like a native of the island. It was a fair bus ride out from the beach, but she enjoyed the experience and soon felt very comfortable jumping on and off various buses and routes to arrive at Maspalomas. Within two minutes of her arrival at the beach the first evening, she bumped into four different people from two countries she had met on past trips.

The second day without Jesus began early. Lou had breakfast at his place. It consisted of fruit and yoghurt that he had left for her. She gathered her towel, sun cream and money together and made her way to the beach. After some basking in the glorious sunshine, she overheard some familiar voices. She couldn't quite believe it when she looked around and had her suspicions confirmed. Of all people this international haven brought to its shores, she ran into the German 'birthday club' who she usually met in November at her favourite place. By chance they were all out there now in May! What a result.

It was so good to catch up with them. What a lovely surprise.

And so, Lou concluded, that despite Jesus only spending half her short break with her, she still managed to amuse herself and enjoy her favourite place (even without having more sex while he was gone). She enjoyed dinner with her Irish friend Declan and beach time with the German contingent. It turned out to be quite a mixed holiday, but one she thoroughly enjoyed for different reasons. It was hard not to have a good time in Gran Canaria really, as she found out every time!

Chapter 15 – Winning the chase

Lou always liked to take care of her body and this meant frequent visits to the gym, which was conveniently located next door to her work. When she didn't have her youngest children at home, she would be straight in there when it opened at 0630, where there would usually be a queue to enter. It seemed that many others had the same idea: to get the exercise done before the real day started. It was one thing to tick off the busy list of things to do.

Lou was also a 'self-confessed fattist' which was possibly a term she had created herself, but she just couldn't understand how people could let themselves go and have so little respect for themselves that they would cram on the pounds and eat their way to middle age and beyond. It was different if there was a medical condition, but Lou found that there were far too many people around stating they were 'curvy' when in fact they were just fat. Lou just didn't comprehend it at all and was therefore not attracted to either.

However Lou did have huge amounts of respect for were those who were trying to get themselves back into a healthier lifestyle and she would always encourage this. Any type of self-improvement in Lou's eyes had to be a good thing and to be commended; whether that was weight-loss, giving up smoking, taking up yoga, meditating and the like. For Lou, she didn't want to look like she had four children. She wanted to have a slim body, although she knew that slight extra 'mummy belly' seemed nigh on impossible to eradicate. It was a common complaint when the abdominal muscles don't sew back together post-delivery, but Lou was very conscious of it and tried her utmost to keep it at bay (which was slightly hampered by her sweet tooth). This meant frequent trips to the gym and when possible throwing in Zumba for cardio, which happened to be a lot of fun too, particularly as Sammy the instructor had a passion for dancing and laughter in her classes. Lou recently started pole fitness too, which was proving fantastic for her core strength and toning.

Whilst at the gym, Lou would normally have her Bluetooth headphones securely in place as she took up her usual position of the second stepper on the left. She treated it almost like a spin bike in that she would alter her rhythm with the music she was playing and her legs would take care of themselves. Lou did wonder how much longer this would be her machine of choice as her left knee had recently started to creak a little. Oh the joys of getting older eh? For now, she would continue as it seemed to burn the calories quicker than the treadmill and she'd always come off it in a dripping sweat, which she knew was a bit of a turn on for some gym-goers. She'd been asked before not to shower after the gym with at least two men she had played with, but they were in slightly different contexts and had nothing to do with going back to the office after.

Knowing that muscle tone also deteriorates as you mature, Lou had recently started using the weight machines after her cardio, focusing mainly on arms and legs. It was since then that she'd found herself in a different area within the gym, where free weights were a-plenty, as were the abundance of muscly young men, who were also there to improve or maintain their bodies. They certainly made her viewing choices more interesting that early in the day, especially as there were all shapes and colours, all with the same goal.

One Adonis who caught Lou's eye was black, around thirty-five and fit as fuck! There didn't appear to be a gram of fat on his body and he had the triangular back she adored. She wanted to speak with him, but it was made a little tricky as he always trained with another guy (who was also rather pleasing on the eye). There were a couple of times Lou tried to make eye contact, but they were both too engrossed in their training. Lou knew it would happen. She had a goal now, not that she was in any rush, and that was just as well because it took some time to crack this nut.

Since first spying him in the gym, Lou also crossed paths with him in her work's reception. It seemed they shared the same employer as well as the same gym. He looked hot in his tailored suit and polished shoes. The defined chest bulging through his crisp white shirt was a good look, which she most definitely approved of. He certainly did know how to take care of himself. Hot hot hot! It just made her want him more, but she was playing the patient game. Their time would come. She was somehow sure of this even though she never knew his name, his marital status, his sexuality or in fact anything about him at all. He hadn't even acknowledged her yet, which made this all the more of a challenge for Lou and she liked a challenge.

The key to progressing with this hunt was familiarity and frequency of getting herself noticed. This would mean putting herself in front of him on any occasion and the only semi-guaranteed location for this would be back at the gym. Instead of stretching out on the big mats, Lou decided to position herself in the other matted area located in between the weights and the cardio equipment. How very convenient indeed for displaying how flexible she was and perhaps spending a little longer straddled and lengthening those hamstrings. She didn't have to look at anyone to sense it was well received by those around her, well at least she hoped so. It was taking a lot of effort to be this bendy, which was mutually beneficial.

It was still a few weeks later that they finally made some form of contact. Alternating childcare meant Lou didn't always get to the gym early, so this was bound to take a while. When it finally happened, Lou had swapped her machine of choice for power walking at a gradient, so she had built up a sweat, but her clothes weren't sticking to her body as such. Her face was still a healthy pink, but not the beetroot red it would normally be post-stepper. This was probably a blessing given the proceedings that followed, which all be they minimal, were the start.

Lou had made her way to the construction she

called the 'jet pack'. She had no idea what its true name was, but she used it for strengthening her abdominal muscles as she brought her knees up to tuck position from hanging. (This was all in preparation for her shoulder mount on the pole, which was proving difficult to achieve so the extra conditioning at the gym would help with this recently acquired objective.) And there he was on the leg raiser machine just to her left in front. She was looking directly at him as she began her set of three times ten curls. He was looking strong and he meant business with his work out, which she adored. No point being in the gym unless you're giving 100%.

As he finished his set and removed himself from the contraption, he turned and faced Lou. This was her opportunity to pounce, albeit subtly. Their eyes met and she nodded her head, "Alright?" He smiled and nodded back with the same greeting. That was enough. It was all that was needed now to move on to the next stage in her careful planning. This meant that every time she now saw him, the gate was open to hold further dialogue with him, even if it would casually be a one-word salutation for a while and Lou was fine with that. She had enough other male interests at the moment that she would enjoy this slow simmering one for however long it took.

As it transpired, it was a good couple of months before Lou resumed the game. She had been on a couple of trips (business and pleasure) and unfortunately missed her usual morning exercise slot on a number of occasions. Now she found herself back in the routine, she happened upon him again and decided to step up the pursuit, beginning with a "Hey, how are you doing?" He looked pleased with her approach, even if on this occasion she had completed forty minutes on the stepper and had nearly thrown up after going in too strong too early. Maybe he was another one who likes the salty, sweaty taste of a workout well done? Either way, he was smiling when he told her he was well. Lou hadn't realised until that point that he was very well spoken. The attraction levels were increasing for Lou. He was proving to be delicious on the eye, a sharp dresser and sounding delightful too. She was going to have to move this one along a little more quickly than she'd first anticipated, but without blatantly throwing herself at him.

It was a few more mini conversations like this at the gym before the full-on attack took place. Lou knew from these interactions that he was interested, albeit he was coming across as coy and reserved. Fortunately Lou's 'Playdar' was seldom wrong, if ever. (The only time it had proved indifferent was when a married man would suddenly remember his morals and decide not to flirt with her any further, which Lou respected.) His eyes were certainly more sparkly and engaging as they chatted in the gym, as minimal as those conversations were. In fact 'conversations' is probably over-egging them. It was the usual exchange of a few words and mainly discretely staring at each other's bodies while training.

A few days passed and having been to a meeting on a different floor within the building, Lou spied him in the main lobby area. Walking confidently and looking hot in a tight pink shirt, Lou decided to make her move. (Obviously he had suit trousers on too, but Lou was drawn to his bulging muscles that immediately caught her eye.) Seeing him striding in her direction, she altered her path and walked straight up to him and grabbed both of his wrists. Initially he looked stunned. Calmly Lou smiled and bashfully said "So...? When are we going for that drink?" It was the most words she'd ever said to him and for a moment she wondered if it was the right choice, as he was looking somewhat perplexed. If he was gay, then Lou was going to feel pretty stupid any moment now. Fortunately his face cracked into a beautiful smile. "Shit. Sorry. I didn't recognise you in your work clothes. You look different. I'm used to seeing you in your gym kit. Do you even know my name?" Lou was beaming now too. Thank goodness the reaction was feeling positive. "Well no actually, but I just knew I had to ask." Lou was pleased she had as he told her his name and she did the same. She would contact him on the internal messaging system as he was on route to a meeting.

'Phew. That went well' Lou mused on the way back to her desk. His name was Blane. He had told her and it was a good solid name. Lou also knew that Blane would be feeling equally as pleased with himself as she did. Lou thought it was a win-win as far as she was concerned, even if it went no further than the encounter they had already shared. It was enough to make them happy for the rest of the day.

Lou found him on the work system and didn't

bother wasting any time in dropping him her first message. It would be waiting for him upon his return. There was no point in playing games. She'd already been forward enough not to care about such things. "Great to finally meet you, even if I did have to accost you downstairs." That would do it. It was just really to give him access to her and to save him having to hunt her down himself. Some twenty minutes later came the response, "Well I'm glad you did." Boom! They were on the same page and she knew it!

The conversation started mainly about the gym and their shared love of it and then moved quickly on to tattoos and body appreciation. Some mild flirting quickly ensued when Lou suggested they grab a coffee and chat in person. It would be far easier to talk face to face and then she could enjoy staring at him too (which she kept to herself, for now at least. She didn't want to be blowing too much smoke up his arse). It was a fast negotiation and less than five minutes later they were in the coffee bar queue on a different floor grabbing a drink. Lou joked about Blane's face when she walked up to him. He had calmed down now and was looking far more chilled. He said that as well as her looking different clothed, he'd only ever seen her with her hair up, so that too was different. Once he'd looked into her lovely eyes, as he put it, the penny dropped and he had realised who she was.

Drinks in hand, Blane suggested they see if a meeting room was available so they could speak more openly. As luck would have it, there had been a 'no show' so a room was free for them.

Unfortunately, someone was in it when they approached. Lou thought they might have to have a logistical re-think, but Blane bowled straight in and asked them to leave. Lou admired his confidence.

Once in the room, the pair of them sat down next to each other. Blane was a little cautious and opened with stating he was in a relationship that was coming to an end and wasn't looking to get into another one. With his stall laid out, Lou said, "That's fine. I'm not into relationships either. I'm just about having fun." With that in the open, he appeared to both physically and mentally relax. His posture changed subtly and then the fun conversation began.

Blane was curious as to what attracted Lou to him and why she had made the approach. He was obviously fishing for compliments, so naturally, Lou was brutally honest and told it exactly as it was. "Well, I won't lie. Call me shallow, but it's your body. You're fucking hot!" There – it was said! Blane was radiant now. It was just what he wanted to hear. He confessed that he had spotted Lou in the gym ages ago and often had a cheeky stare at her while she was exercising. (Lou's cunning plan had worked it appeared, as she knew it would!)

Lou's cheeky demeanour continued as they learned more about one another and it took no time at all before they were talking about what they would like to do to each other instead. 'Wow. That was quick,' Lou thought, and with them both being very decisive, plans were made rapidly, jumping straight to a hotel meet the following week! They knew they were both blatantly attracted and wanted to explore each other's bodies, so why not?

No physical contact took place in the room. Their only touch had been earlier when Lou had grabbed his wrists in the lobby. Lou would have to wait until after work the following Tuesday. With over a week to go, Lou knew that time would surely drag. Returning to her desk, a message was already waiting for her. "You really have brought sparkle to an otherwise dull Monday. Looking forward to next week already." And so was she.

The following day Lou saw Blane holding a meeting at the coffee area. Once again he was looking gorgeous and he kept it professional as he caught her eye and smiled. Lou herself was meeting Pearls of Wisdom (POW from *Vanilla Extract*) for a tea and catch up. She had already shared her story with POW, so it was quite handy seeing Blane there so she could point him out. Lou had told her old friend about her plans of seducing him a while back. Now he could compare her descriptions of the body beautiful with the real thing and being a very active and very fit specimen himself; POW appreciated his form.

Lou wondered if Blane would speak to her as his meeting ended. She was pleased he did, even if it was a little lame about non-gym attendance that day. Both of them knew it was more of an acknowledgement. POW commented afterwards that the lady Blane had met was equally 'do-able' and Lou agreed. A potential foursome in the making perhaps - but that was just the way their two minds worked. She and POW shared very similar thinking when it came to the opposite sex and sex with each other! (And it was only a matter of time before this pairing came together again. Albeit a year or so since their last steamy session, the chemistry and tension was electric between them. It always had been, even if they had shared a break from each other's loins.)

Over the next few days, Lou and Blane exchanged some messages on the work messenger system and outside of work on Whatsapp. It was all going swimmingly until things took a different turn. It seemed that Blane acquired cold feet as their date grew closer. It came as quite a shock to Lou as he'd been so keen over the past few exchanges. "Look Lou. I'm really flattered by your proposal, but as I mentioned, I am coming out of a relationship and have a lot going on at the moment. I'm going to have to decline, as you really wouldn't get the best from me right now. I'm sorry to have messed you around. I hope you understand." Well, that was a surprise. Lou was taken aback but didn't want to appear desperate, even though she was a little disappointed. This meant that either he was genuine and needed time to get his shit together at home or it could all be a bunch of lies and he wasn't at the turning point in a relationship at all. He might be happily coasting along in one but had been tempted by her forbidden fruit and got carried away with the ego-boosting flattery. "No worries babe and I do understand. Just give me a shout when you're back in the zone." Despite the message, Lou wasn't giving up on him. The chemistry was too strong to ignore and she knew it was just a matter of time before she found out how this would play out. Tick tock, tick tock.

Lou was right too. The following Monday came along and Lou had been to the gym later than normal, having had to drop her kids off at their dad's before work. It was now almost 11:30 and she was gasping for a white Americano when she messaged him on the off chance. "I need a coffee. If you fancy one, then I'll be heading down to the cafe shortly." It was innocent enough and she had no idea how he'd respond. She didn't have a moment to wait as the instant message returned with, "You grab a meeting room, and I'll bring the coffees." She liked his style!

It seemed like Lou was only sat in the room for a couple of minutes before Blane arrived. As usual, he was looking smoking hot, this time in the return of a crisp white figure-hugging shirt. Damn, he looked good. What a waste! "Well hello there. Fancy seeing you here," he exclaimed as he entered. "You're looking divine." Lou thanked him as he sat down next to her and the conversation struck up seamlessly. Blane apologised once more for his situation and Lou explained hers. Ultimately Lou understood the circumstances he had described to her (even if they were fabricated or not, as the case may be) but she added, "It doesn't stop me wanting you." He looked pleased with this declaration and his eyes told her that he felt the same way. His constant staring at her legs also revealed what he was thinking. He couldn't take his eyes off them. What caused the next reaction was probably Lou adding that she would still quite happily have had him bend her over the meeting table before them and for him to pummel her frantically on it. This seemed to ignite some fuse within him and the desire took hold.

Blane suddenly got up, walked to the door and locked it. "Stand up Lou," he instructed. 'This is a turn of events,' she thought and instantly complied. How could she resist? Without any further words, they both went in for the kiss at the same time. It was powerful. It was passionate. His lips were all over her mouth and she was nibbling at them as he was biting on hers. Their tongues were like snakes curling up and around each other, sending shock waves through both their bodies at the same time. Damn this was hot and not what she'd expected at all. There she was thinking she'd flirt more vigorously and show him what he'd decided to miss out on and instead they were full on and eating each other's faces!

Lou's hand wandered south and felt the bulge in his trousers. It seemed he was packing down there as well as all over everywhere else. Wow - what a body! She couldn't wait to have it naked, but not in this room! He appeared not to care about their location and was determined to fuck her right here and right now. He turned her around and lifted her dress. This revealed the beautiful basque Lou was wearing. ('Result!' Lou thought as she had planned her underwear accordingly for her play date that evening after work. Blane was not to know that and would happily believe she always wore this attire beneath her office clothes.) Lou was quite surprised when she heard him undo his zip. He really did think he was going to have her here. Sadly that was not going to happen. "Sorry babe, but not without protection." Now it was his turn to be taken aback, but she could understand why he looked flummoxed. "Oh shit. Sorry. I didn't even think about it. I've only had sex with one woman for so long that it didn't even cross my mind. Fuck, sorry!" It was fine. They both appreciated the predicament they were in. It would not be resolved in this instance. But it could be...

Lou confessed she had some condoms in her bag upstairs. She always had some onboard (particularly as she was 'on a promise' that night). If the two of them were still 'game on' she could go get one and they could continue this naughty liaison. Fearful that the interruption would have killed the moment, Lou was pleased that he was far from letting this situation stop there. "Go do it and I'll book another room." And like lightening, she was off!

Lou took a moment to pop to the loo whilst on her work floor. Checking everything was in order with her underwear and boobs lifted back into place, she headed back to see him, with small purse securely held in her palm with its saviour content. His Whatsapp message revealed the new room, but when she arrived there she found it was even more exposed than the last. It was closer to a corridor where rooms were used more frequently for customer interviews. This was not going to work. During this time too, Blane seemed to have developed a wobble about the surroundings and rightly too Lou agreed. "Trust me. I know somewhere else," and with that, Lou led him back to the lifts.   Having worked in this building long enough, Lou had found all sorts of places where mischief could take place.

Maintaining their formal appearance, the two of them made their way to an external meeting floor that was for the higher net worth customers. When the building was first erected, it had contained an in-house apartment for board members to stay when they flew over from Sydney and other countries. But due to cuts in the travel budget and the need for space, this area had been converted into more useable facilities (meeting rooms and office space). The indulgent bathrooms, however, had remained and this was where the horny pair was heading. Blane never once questioned her knowledge of such things: too deep was the desire to copulate at that moment in time.

In the lift, Lou looked at the lift display and had a moment of panic. It was 12:20. "Shit! I'm due in a meeting in ten minutes!" For an instant in her mind she debated a whole number of different considerations:

1. Should she abandon this crazy scenario and head back to her desk for the meeting? (But it was just too horny not to continue.)
2. Should she cut this impending naughtiness very short once they'd got going? (That would never happen, and she would have to continue it to completion.)
3. Should she postpone it until later? (See above.)
4. Should she continue as was and see where this led? (And face the consequences about the meeting later.)

In the split second of considering her options, Blane piped up with, "Looks like you're going to be late for your meeting then." It was a decision she had already made but he now reaffirmed in Lou's mind.

Once inside the marble-lined bathroom, the passionate kissing continued. Lou didn't give him a chance to make the next move. She reached down, unzipped his trousers and removed his enlarged member from within. It was a good size and it was going straight into her mouth – no question about that! Onto her knees, she descended and began to give him the pleasure he longed for. He let out a very satisfying gasp as she looked up he was biting his own lip this time. He was enjoying the attention. Lou wondered how long it had been since he'd been so spontaneous or had a mouth so passionately around his cock.

More sighs were freed now and he must have realised the sounds he was making. He reached over and turned a tap on. It was a wise move as it camouflaged his admissions of pleasure as people walked past the other side of the door. If only they knew what was going on this side of it. (It was probably best they didn't though as they could both lose their jobs!)

Lou got up and removed her dress. She didn't want to return to her desk with her clothes all screwed up. That would be an instant give away! Blane removed his shirt for the same reason. It was the first time she had seen his tattooed chest exposed and it looked delicious. Wow. What a body! Blane was equally admiring Lou's and it was not long before he wanted to take her. "Where's that condom?" He asked eagerly. Lou took it out of the purse and handed it to him. She turned around, lent over the marble sink and watched their reflection in anticipation. With protection firmly in place, Blane entered her slowly. He felt good as he slid inside to the top. "Oh fuck!" Lou said quietly due to her surroundings and then the frantic pounding began.

Blane certainly wanted her. He made that evidently clear by his animalistic taking of her. After the initial entry, he forced himself in and out aggressively, holding firmly on her hips. It was not in any way painful for Lou. She was already moist from the build-up in the last forty minutes or so - not that she ever had an issue with self-lubrication. The pummeling was exciting because it had been unexpected, but also because of the risk of being found in this compromising situation. How very rude indeed! She loved it!

In the mirror, Lou noticed the sweat building on his forehead as he held her over the sink, his hands now making their way to her hair, where they grabbed and pulled it as he continued to fuck her. It was getting very hot in here and not just the temperature. She looked at his face and saw a new look she'd not seen before. It was pure. It was passion, and he wore it well. Damn, he was sexy and just her type!

Changing positions, Lou decided to let him have a break. He grabbed some tissue and wiped his brow. She was going to move to the toilet and have him sit down upon it, but that's where their folded clothes had been placed earlier. Instead she gestured for him to get down on the floor. It was cooler there anyway on the tiles. He sat with his back against the wall as she straddled his legs and began to squat up and down. Blane was nodding in approval. "Ooh, that's good. Yes, that's right! Good girl!" Lou continued. It was feeling good for her too. He was a good size and she could feel every quiver inside her. Unfortunately the hard floor would have been too painful for her to move from her feet to her knees, as she would have liked to switch to more manic riding.

"You're going to have to get up soon or I'm gonna come." Lou didn't need any other words. She immediately stood up and said, "Well you'd best fill me up over the sink then." It meant she could watch them both in action again, which was a sexy sight to behold. It also meant easy access to tissue and water for as and when required, which wouldn't be long. (And there she was with her practical head on again!)

Blane was building up for the finale whilst at the same time trying to control the volume of the noise he was making. It was all quite amusing for Lou, as she derived pleasure from watching his dilemma as well as enjoying his manly thrusting. Harder and harder he pumped until there it was. Pulling her hips back towards him, he let her have his load. He couldn't help but let a moan out, even if it was muffled against his right bicep.

Next came the first moment of calm they had shared for some time. He was frozen inside her for just a few seconds that felt like way more, as his body resumed its normal functionality. Now he was smirking. It was a cross between mild embarrassment and looking very pleased with himself: which he rightly deserved. Lou returned the look. She was feeling equally as naughty as he was.

Now came the practical measures of disposing of the evidence and cleaning up, which they both did as a matter of course. Smiling at each other somewhat churlishly in the mirror, they both proceeded to get dressed and return to their corporate attire. How very matter of fact! Blane turned the tap off finally and Lou indicated she would leave the 'crime scene' first. It was difficult for them both not to burst into laughter, but somehow they managed to contain themselves.

Lou headed back to the lifts and didn't concern herself with Blane's departure. Walking confidently, she tried hard not to look like she had been up to no good, but the glowing smile would be a dead give-away to anyone that knew of her naughty side. In fact, she had the same look on her face for the rest of the day and apparently so did Blane. They messaged later and Lou joked with him on the messenger: "Last week I made your Monday sparkle. A week later and I've made you..." The smiley emoji was returned. "You most certainly did that."

Chapter 16 – A better underground encounter

A previous unexpected meeting on a busy London underground tube train had led from excited anticipation to disappointment quite rapidly, but this did not deter Lou from any future encounters on this mode of transport. In fact on the next occasion of this variety, Lou wasn't even supposed to be on the rails at this time of day. Rather spontaneously, she had decided to visit a friend who was in hospital, and that meant tackling both the Jubilee and Northern underground lines.

One stop into Lou's journey and a rather energetic looking man boarded and took up the seat diagonally opposite her. Now every seat was taken, which she was surprised at this late in the morning. It was 10:45am and the usual bustle of corporate commuting had settled down a fair bit, but these were other workers and visitors going about their business.

The new passenger looked European, with shaggy black hair (David Grohl-style) and matching beard. His eyes were a very dark brown and were sparkling with mischief. He was wearing a black baggy t-shirt, but she couldn't help notice the arms were tight on his rather bulging arms. She could see the muscle definition as the sleeve edge clung to the flesh. (Obviously this was an instant hit for Lou, who was partial to a well-toned male.)

Lou didn't take any notice of what he was wearing on his legs, probably joggers, because she was so drawn to his eyes. They were glistening as she saw him looking across. He almost looked puzzled. Lou caught his eye and then looked away. She could sense him looking at her legs, which were rather tanned from a recent holiday and were crossed. Her peep-toe shoes revealed a mint coloured nail polish, matching her fingers, and her silver ankle bracelet finished her right leg off perfectly. (It came out every summer and despite having it for years and years, it always drew attention – normally from women asking where she'd bought it from.)

Lou looked down the semi-crowded carriage and at him as her eyes swept back up again. A second time she caught him staring, but this time she maintained the gaze for a bit longer. He still looked like he was trying to work something out or was he just taking her all in? It was difficult to tell, but he was certainly embarrassed that she was still looking back at him. He broke a huge smile, exposing perfect (but natural) white teeth and when she returned the gesture, he gave her a quick wink.

"Are you staring at me?" Lou asked confidently, despite all the other commuters clearly listening in. He smiled back but was still looking a little confused. He nodded and then gave a thumbs up to her. 'Well he's a bit of a cutie,' Lou thought. She didn't want this moment to end, so she quite clearly told him she was getting off at the next station. He immediately jumped up and went to the door in anticipation of the stop ahead. Lou decided to do the same and they found themselves at the end of the carriage now speaking with one another.

"You are the most beautiful woman I have seen on the tube," he began. "Your eyes, your legs, your smile. You are so beautiful." Respectfully, Lou thanked him for his compliments and asked him where he was from. He had a strong, delectable accent but she couldn't place it. "I am from Roma and I have lived in England for the past three years. What about you?" Lou told him of her heritage and that she had just returned from an Italian sightseeing trip with her children. He looked impressed. "Very good, very good. Is it ok if we speak on the platform when the train stops?" he asked and Lou was glad he did, as the window between carriages was already lowered and wind was gusting through it, sending her long hair all over her face and in her mouth. It wasn't exactly ideal and certainly did nothing to assist her charm offensive in any capacity whatsoever.

As the train pulled in to London Bridge, this unlikely couple moved into the area between platforms where they could speak more conveniently. His name was Lenny and he told her he was very pleased that Lou had smiled back at him. He had not heard her question about him staring across at her, as he had headphones in on the train, which was partly why he was looking a little off-guard earlier.

"I would very much like to take you out for a drink or dinner, or for anything actually, if you will let me." Lou didn't need any time to consider. She knew that she definitely wanted to follow this up as well. However, her busy childfree weekend was already packed with plans, and her kids were returning on Monday. She was due to be back in the area on the next day to collect her car, if he was available for lunch. "I will make myself available for you any time." ('Typical Italian man,' Lou thought. They certainly pulled no punches when it came to being charming, even if that was a huge generalisation.)

Once a time was agreed they shared a hug. It was a very close one, with both of them pulling each other in tight. Lou could feel his tight body and muscles bulging. He grabbed her waist and held her firmly. She swept her left arm up behind him and placed it on the back of his head. His long hair was damp. "Have you just been to the gym?" Lou asked him. "No, I am just out of the shower. I am on my way to work." Lou wondered if he worked in London Bridge but it transpired he was off to Bond Street. She melted when he told her he was a massage therapist and it must have shown because he was smiling even more broadly now and nodding again. "Your massages will be free." 'Hell yes!' Lou thought and laughed. She would definitely be taking him up on that one!

Lenny took her phone number in case anything changed overnight and would affect their arrangement, but it was also so they could both begin some banter ahead of their meeting, which didn't take long at all to get started. It was by the time they were above ground again where they both had a signal. The messaging was of mutual appreciation and excitement for the next day.

As her workday continued, Lou was almost convinced that her date for the evening would cancel. He seemed a bit flaky and in some respects, she was hoping it would be postponed. Lenny was definitely on her mind and she had a feeling he would be waiting for her to say just that: "My plans have changed. Why don't we have dinner tonight instead?" Lou was very tempted. She decided to give the other fella until 5pm. If no concrete plans were made, Lenny would be getting her full attention tonight.

At 4.45pm her prior engagement was back on Whatsapp and confirming the arrangements for the evening. Lenny would have to wait after all. It would only be a few more hours until lunch tomorrow at noon. (Fortunately Lou had a fantastic evening with the man she met. It was probably because she was half expecting it to be a lame night, due to her considering other options, but that was not the case what so ever.)

After three hours of sleep, Lou made her way back to Canary Wharf. She was feeling a little jaded and wanted to appear her best for Lenny. This was a struggle, given she was physically and mentally exhausted, but she couldn't fault a good night. They certainly had partied!

Lou had warned Lenny that she would be in casual attire today and not the smart black and peach figure-hugging dress she had on yesterday. The black patent peep toe heels would also not be featuring; instead swapping for open, flat (but still stylish) black sandals instead. It was a glorious day in London and her choice of strappy vest and colourful flowing skirt felt very comfortable indeed in this heat.

Lou had a touch of the bohemian air about her and Lenny instantly praised her when they met outside the station. "You look beautiful – so feminine and womanly and these colours bring out the blue of your eyes." 'Oh he's good,' Lou thought and happily exchanged a cuddle with him. His tight grey top was sculpted to his physique and showed every line and projection from underneath. She could see his shaved chest just poking out. He was perfect. Lou also knew that a few 'unicorn' friends of hers would have wanted to lick him all over at that point! He was looking irresistible.

'Some decorum please,' Lou reminded herself. While this was a Saturday, and she was unlikely to see anyone from work, she still should maintain a level of control. There were families in the area enjoying the great weather after all.

Lenny suggested a number of restaurants (which she knew, having worked there for the past sixteen years, not that he was to know that) and of all choices, they decided on Italian. They grabbed a seat outside and continued their discovery of each other. Lou was a little embarrassed as he was openly full of compliments and she was glad the people on the table next to them were engrossed in their own worlds so as not to take any notice. (And when I say they were occupying themselves, it wasn't by talking to each other, but spending their entire lunch messaging other people on their phones. When did lives become so sad that people don't even enjoy spending time with the people they lunch with?)

This pairing, however, couldn't get enough of each other and were talking about spending some 'quality' time together as soon as possible. Lou was pretty sure that the date she had planned for the following evening would be cancelled. (Her rather delicious scaffolder friend was being kept in hospital for longer than anticipated following an operation and was very unlikely to be out a day later.) She decided to take a gamble on that outcome and booked Lenny in for Sunday night after he finished work. This allowed her to recover from a club night in Colchester on the Saturday with someone else! Lou certainly did know how to fill her time and enjoyed being a social butterfly. That was for sure.

After their food, they moved on to Jubilee Park where they intended to continue their conversation in the sunshine, or rather shade as it turned out. The sun was sweltering. The park was again full of families having fun. Lou wondered if it was always like this at the weekends or whether some event had brought them all out. It was certainly buzzing with children's activities, so they continued their walk through it and headed instead to Canada Square and found the quieter benches there.

Despite being close to work, Lou felt comfortable enough to sit next to Lenny and then to drape her legs across his. This brought them closer and naturally in for a kiss. It was then that Lou noticed his animal passion. His hands were all over her cheeks and dragging her face into his as his tongue thrashed with hers. Saliva was generated quickly as they collided and bodies locked tight. 'Whoa, he's really eating my face!' Lou thought and while enjoying the desire she was also conscious that her employer's building was looming over her. All she needed was one of the security guards to walk past and she would have been mortified! She often chatted to them in work, so that would have been just a tad embarrassing!

Reining it in ever so slightly, she reminded Lenny that this was where she worked, albeit during the week and not the weekends. He was very respectful. "I am sorry Lou. You are just so beautiful. I want to have you – every piece of you." And he would have. There was no doubt in her mind about that, but not here. "We just have to wait one more day," she reminded him. He knew, but he wanted her now! 'Sexy fucker!' Lou thought and he was. "Would you like the massage first or the sex first tomorrow Lou?" After pondering his directness, she wondered. It was a tough one. She opted for the massage but was fully aware there would be no guarantee the events would take this order. Lou knew that the moment itself would decide.

Their conversation moved on to how attracted Lenny had always been to the more mature lady. He had lost his virginity at a very early age, to a woman old enough to be his mother. Lou had found the same with other younger men who preferred a cougar or MILF (Mother I'd Like to Fuck). They were introduced to sex by someone who had years of experience. This seemed to stay with them and the women they were attracted to came with no intentions for marriage or (more) children and a more balanced and liberated attitude to sex.

After a few more kisses and nibbles of each other's necks, it was time to part company. Unlike the movies, there was no furtive looking back. Instead, Lou had to pop into the supermarket and pick up some cat food before driving back. Lenny sauntered off and made his way to wherever he was going next. Who says romance is dead 'eh?

Saturday night proved eventful too and it was certainly a night to remember. Lou had never been to a club before where a sole protester stood outside being a nuisance to those entering. She thought he needed to get a life, as what harm could there be in consenting people engaging in sexual fun? She also wondered if he just perved there at the people going in so that he had more wank bank material to use when he got home? Who knew? "There's now't funnier than folk," as they say!

It was great for Lou to reconnect with the club owners she had met a month or so ago in Gran Canaria, and they had a good boogie with her and other guests. It was probably the smallest club she had attended, but the clientele were fun and certainly knew how to enjoy themselves.

On Sunday morning Lou woke at stupid o'clock. It was a term she had developed when waking at the likes of 6am on a day off. Why oh why did her body clock do this to her? She was shattered but still found herself awake. Fortunately her guest was also awake and they managed to occupy themselves for a few hours before he headed off.

Lou caught up with her social media and what her friends had been up to overnight. Sitting there in her kitchen she asked herself, "If you are feeling so tired, why don't you get some more sleep?" She had always found it hard to switch off and definitely suffered with 'fear of missing out' but this was different. She had an empty house with no kids and no visitors, and no plans until later that day. Lou took an executive decision and headed back up to bed. Stripped off, toilet visited and back under the covers: it was bliss. And there she stayed for three hours, which was unheard of. She needed it. Three hours was like an extra half a night's sleep for Lou.

Feeling thoroughly refreshed, Lou hit the shower and felt even better. She decided to drive all the way to Lenny's in New Cross, which was just over an hour away. There was parking too, which meant she had no deadline for getting away in the morning, although she did have the rush hour build-up of traffic to contend with.

Alas, her car's satnav had other ideas about exactly where his postcode was located and sent her somewhere quite close. Thank goodness for alternative tools, that ensured she arrived right outside his door, where he was already waiting. He guided her to a parking space opposite (not that she needed assistance) and opened her door up for her once stationary.

Lenny was dressed in casual shorts and a black vest. He was in his socks without shoes and as he came out to greet her he took her bag without question. What a gent! His mother had brought him up well, with impeccable manners. His hair was masked with a navy beanie and he looked sultry, or was that just Lou over-thinking? A kiss was planted next, with another firm hug. "I am so pleased you have come to see me. You look beautiful." It was certainly his preferred word of choice, but looking like he did, he was easily forgiven its over-use. Lou also had to remind herself that English was his second language and was far better than her Italian.

Once inside his bedroom of the shared house, there was no holding back. She barely walked through the door when he was upon her. Given it was a dress she would be wearing to the office the next day, she wanted to carefully hang it somewhere, but he had other intentions. Lou dragged it over her head and he grabbed it and cast it aside. "No – I need that for work tomorrow." He apologised and then grabbed a hanger for it and placed it in his wardrobe. And so back to the onslaught!

Lenny's hunger was fierce! His tongue was deep inside her mouth and with his arms around her hips he lifted her onto the bed. He was in awe of her matching underwear but wished for no obstruction. They were coming off. Lou unbuckled her bra to assist and was nonchalantly carefree in slinging that across the room, soon followed by her knickers!

Now Lenny had complete access and he wasted no time in gaining it! Straight to her pussy he headed and was soon buried deep. Lou wriggled around in pleasure, but she could tell from his eagerness that he wanted to fuck her more than giving oral. That was not a problem, but she wanted him to slow down a tad. They had all night after all.

"Lenny, you get on the bed now. I want to taste you." And there was that glorious smile again. He complied instantly.

His body was truly wondrous and Lou took great pleasure in teasing him with her tongue. Lenny breathed in deeply as she took her time and he enjoyed her full attention. His penis was a good size and after a while of teasing around it, Lenny was holding it up for her in anticipation, but she wasn't succumbing just yet. Lou was enjoying his reactions: gasps, moans and "Oh my god" comments were flowing aplenty now. He relented and put his hands to the side. This was when Lou took him firmly with her left hand and devoured his cock whole. Well that was the intention anyway. It turned out that there was still an inch or so left when she deep-throated him and she was soon gagging on his member. Lenny's back arched instantly and he told her she was a good girl, which Lou thought a little odd given the age difference.

Now his hand was on the back of her head, wanting it again and she continued until she was a spluttering mess with mascara now running. Her eyes were certainly watering and he delighted in it. Lou maintained a delicate touch now, using the slippery saliva that was created, gently sliding up and down his shaft. At the top, her mouth was sometimes waiting and other times it was just her hand that was doing the work. Lenny was in heaven but he wanted more. "Give me your pussy. Let's 69," and they did. Both enjoying each other's swollen members, their oral pleasure giving and taking was at an all-time high.

CINNAMON TWIST

Lou could sense that he wanted to be inside her. She was thinking the same. "I think you need to fuck me, Lenny." A massive smile appeared. "You want I wear a condom?" Of course she did and miraculously one appeared very swiftly on the end of his rather keen cock.

Lenny placed his arms either side of her ribcage and entered her slowly, touching her skin with his arms and maintaining eye contact beneath those dark locks of hair. She noticed the outline of his muscles projecting as he held his weight above her and slid in and out. There was no need for lubrication. Her anticipation had caused this involuntary reaction and her juices had started to flow some time ago. Vigorously his motion sped up and soon he was fucking for his life, it seemed. Lou's legs grabbed around the back of him and locked as his thrusting continued. He murmured in approval. Damn this was heating up as he pounded harder and harder!

Sweat began to form on his body and face, and soon it looked to be escaping down onto Lou. She did not mind in any shape or form. She'd read somewhere along the way that sweaty men were more virile (possibly written by an over-perspiring type she wondered. The same was said about bald men and she pondered the truth in that too).

"I need water," Lenny suddenly exclaimed. He was overheating and needed fresh air and hydration. He grabbed one of the new water bottles carefully thought out earlier and he'd placed on the side for this very moment. Lenny offered it to Lou first and upon her decline, drank a fair bit of it before he

207

reached over and opened the window wider. An instant breeze came flowing in and the combination worked to cool them both down. "Do you mind if we take a break and then continue the sex in ten minutes?" Lou smiled. This was an odd but very prescriptive request. "There's no stress here Lenny. We are together for the night. Let's just relax and do whatever we like. We can take a breather. That's fine. There's no rush." He instantly relaxed and offered her some of the strawberries he'd brought in earlier. He was very mindful of her thoughts and needs, bless him. What a cutie.

Before today, Lenny had asked her what wine she preferred so he could get some in. Considering the weekend that she originally had planned and the one she ended up having, as it worked out, Lou wasn't entirely convinced she would need any more alcohol on Sunday. She wasn't particularly fussed, but in his chivalrous way, Lenny was insistent that he provided her with drink, dinner and a massage (as well as plenty of loving too of course). Lou opted for red and that's just what he was pouring before they got some fresh air in the garden. Lenny took the opportunity to have a smoke and Lou sat with him drinking her wine. It was a chance for them to talk some more and she discovered that he had been a cage fighter in Canada years before. That explained his Adonis-like physique.

It was a welcome respite, as she knew they would be having sex for most of Sunday night. In fact, it wasn't even ten minutes before they were locked into each other once more. It was Lenny's fault! He was the one staring at her and filling her with complimentary confidence, then grabbing the back of her head and forcing a deep kiss. They were both standing and Lou still had the wine in her hand. She carefully held it while their embrace of tongues continued before he realised and helped her guide it to the side. The face 'eating' carried on till he pushed her back on the bed and resumed consumption of her lady parts.

Lou was still not convinced she would have her usual explosive orgasm with him in this way. Maybe it was because her weekend had been rather exhausting, even with the extra sleep she'd stolen that day? Maybe it was because he was that much younger and super energetic that her body perhaps wasn't keeping up with his? The most likely reason was that she didn't know him well enough to give herself fully to him yet. This was all a bit frantic and animalistic, which there was no problem with, but the fanfare, trumpets and confetti may just have to wait for one of their follow-up sessions (of which there definitely would be).

Fresh condom duly adorned, Lenny was filling her up once more and Lou gave her all from below. This surprised him. He did not appear to have had this experience before and as she pumped upwards onto his cock, Lenny smiled down at her in admiration. "Good girl. That's so good," he revelled and enjoyed the sensations as she rode him from beneath. He reached down and kissed her again. This was doing the trick as he frantically pummelled her back and their rhythm was lost for a moment until Lou let him take control once more.

The rest of this wild and steamy session was a blur. They tried just about every position possible, and at one stage Lou thought she would break his squeaky bed as she rode him deep, grinding down onto him till she could go no further. When she joked with him about it, Lenny said his bed always did this. "You mean I am not your only lover?" she laughed, and he looked embarrassed until he understood her humour and smiled back.

At one point, with her head buried in his mattress and her arms drawn up behind herself, Lou said, "I want you to come!" Lou knew that if he continued to fuck her like this for much longer, she would be sore high up inside her. Lenny laughed, "No, I don't want to come yet." 'Oh that's handy,' Lou thought but told him they would have to slow it down as her innards were taking a bashing. The caring and considerate Lenny returned. "Sorry, babe. I didn't realise." It was ok as long as she turned over and either rode him herself or went for 'missionary' instead. The angle and force of the other position definitely wasn't sustainable!

Lou's body was much relieved with the revisited, more comfortable position and a tender Lenny was now entwined with her. He was sensual and affectionate and the slower, exploratory kissing ensued. He was great at this and it was something he enjoyed. He had interrupted all their erratic sex positions with kissing throughout this evening.

The sensual approach didn't last long as it was turning them both on again and like a faucet had opened, Lou switched over to her back so he could resume the intense doggy position once more, but

210

this time without the hands pulled behind. She could sense a change in him. Whereas most men when building up to orgasm tended to get noisier in their gasps and moans, Lenny seemed to withdraw inside himself. Lou assumed that as he had been quite loud throughout, then the volume would have increased, but this was not the case. It was only when the frantic thrusting ceased that she realised he had come. He lay down on her back and cuddled her until he was ready to get up.

Almost instantly Lenny was back in host mode. Now that he had composed himself, he was attentive to her nourishment – this time in the food department. He revealed that before taking up massage, he used to be a chef. 'This guy just gets better and better,' Lou thought to herself. He seemed keen to cook her a beefsteak with broccoli and Lou was not going to decline. She should relax there while he prepared it. Lou was not about to complain! She tucked herself under his duvet and caught up with her social media.

Lenny popped back in a few times to make sure she was ok and to ensure he cooked her food just how she liked it. Medium-rare it would be – "yes, with blood," he confirmed. When he brought it out, Lou thought, 'Is there was no end to this guy's talents?' The food was cooked to perfection. This may have been facilitated by the energetic workout they had shared, but either way, Lou was famished and wolfed it down. It was delicious, but she couldn't finish it all. She was also aware that despite it being past 11pm, she very much doubted their activities were finished for the night. While she would happily have continued eating until the plate was empty, and her stomach was uncomfortably full, Lou knew she would soon be bouncing around again.

Lenny took the tray and placed it on the side. More drinks were offered, but Lou was ok. No sooner had everything been cleared that Lenny was kissing her again. The next round (whatever number this was) began and lasted into the early hours. In the end, Lou had to put in a request for him to come again so that she could get some sleep. She was exhausted and was up early for work the next day. Lenny understood and respectfully asked where exactly she would like him to come. He took off the condom and ejaculated all over her back. It was as much a relief for her as him and soon she was able to drift off to a very deep sleep. She had already warned him of her need to sleep detangled and he complied with that request too, although both of them admitted a day or so later that they had wanted cuddles for longer.

In the morning she had purposely set her alarm for an hour earlier than she needed to wake. Lenny had explained that he was a less chaotic lover in the morning and Lou looked forward to finding out. He was true to his word and even though he did not come, they shared something very special and sensual.

As the time sped away before them, Lou was conscious that she had to get going. Lenny prepared her a Greek yoghurt breakfast with fruit and honey and a fresh coffee. He was a little darling. He even packed her off with a banana for later. What a sweetie.

Lou went off to work, getting stuck in Blackwell Tunnel traffic as she suspected she would do. She managed to get in on time, albeit twenty minutes later than she intended. Lenny was definitely on her mind. She suspected he would have been playing with himself after she left and he confirmed her thoughts, he later told her over lunch at Canary Wharf. It seemed these two could not get enough of one another. They had seen each other daily since their first encounter on the tube and Lou knew it wouldn't be the last time they shared adventures going forward – just as long as he didn't get too needy or obsessed!

Chapter 17 – Exploring the submissive

The random Whatsapp message exchange with her dominant friend Master D would occur every month or so, but it was all quite vague really. It wasn't until one of Lou's Twitter contacts advertised for a dungeon or photo studio that she asked Master D if he was interested. When he said yes, she hooked both parties up to see if they would both benefit from some sort of arrangement.

That was the motivation that caused these two horny fuckers to reconnect once more and for the exploring to recommence. They arranged to meet earlier on in the day that Lou was supposed to be out partying with her Henley friends once again!

"Are you ready to be violated, Lou?" he messaged. Lou was immediately strung out. This was so out of her comfort zone. Initially, she wanted to respond with "No. It ain't gonna happen. There is no way you are ever going to make me feel subservient and I most definitely will not let you take control." It was her natural reaction. Instead, she said, "I'll be honest. It scares me." Master D seemed surprised. "It doesn't scare you. You like coming. You like being fucked with toys and cock. All you are adding is a little restraint and a bit of dominance, in a playroom instead of a bedroom." Lou felt instantly reassured. He was right. These were all things she enjoyed and took pleasure in. Why was she making this something more than it was? Maybe because she knew it was! It was going against all her pre-programming. She was always brought up not to take any shit from anyone, to stand up for herself and to come out fighting. This was the polar opposite of that and the reason why this was freaking her out a little. Well, it had been, until now.

To ease the tension (that perhaps only Lou was feeling), she suggested she arrive around noon, go for some lunch together, maybe at a local pub, and discuss her parameters. He had suggested previously that they work their way through a list he had used ahead of such liaisons. Lou could outline her likes, dislikes and just how far she wanted to explore, so it would be clear to them both what could play out afterwards.

Master D had a slightly different approach. 'I'll make you lunch. We can discuss the list and then you can go into the playroom, remove your clothes and wait for me to come in and start." An instant wave of arousal hit Lou all over. She felt like a hormonal pendulum was swinging throughout her being. One minute she was completely turned on and the next minute full of trepidation. What a very odd combination but one that was beginning to tantalise her.

Lou also loved his way with words. It was direct and it was forceful. It did put her on edge a bit too. She found herself writing a response and then re-writing it. How was it that this man was making her feel so unsettled? No one ever did that. It was part of the attraction – stepping out of her comfort zone.

The date was set. They both understood how this would play out and she would explore the submissive side to understand exactly what they went through at the hands of a dominant person. This was purely research. She wanted to feel every last sensation; every restrained feeling as she lost control and gave herself over to someone else. It was completely and utterly alien, but she was willing to do it so she could speak from experience about it. As a potential future dom, she wanted to understand every morsel of thought and the feelings going through the mind of a sub. She wanted to feel the 'drop' she had heard so much about when your new reality kicks in, for however long you decide. Lou also wanted to explore the irony of the dom being in control when in fact the sub decides when it stops. This was all new learning ground for Lou and she was keen to understand.

As the date was growing closer, Lou was feeling nervous about this planned encounter. It was something she needed to do, but even still, it wasn't lying comfortably with her. She prepared herself mentally and was gearing herself up for this experience when something caught her eye on Facebook. It seemed Master D had started a new relationship and was looking decidedly loved up. Without wishing to pry, Lou wondered if this meant their meeting would not be going ahead now, despite all the planning. She messaged him on Whatsapp, "Congratulations. You're looking good together. I hope it works out for you." It was as much a greeting of goodwill as a reminder of their planned session. Much to her huge disappointment, she heard nothing back from him whatsoever. 'What a bloody let down!' Lou thought. She had been so geared up to try this and she was gutted with his lack of response.

She would move on from this disenchantment and find another dominant figure to help her with her research. Lou still had a lot to learn, even given the many varied and interesting encounters she had experienced of late. Not only that, but there were always boundaries to push and she knew she was only touching the sides on some of those. There were way more kinks to explore and many more countries and clubs to try out too. The world was her oyster and there were no limitations – only the ones she put on herself.

Lou's journey would continue and she was very happy to do so. She certainly wasn't finished yet with her discoveries and adventures.

To be continued…

If you have enjoyed this, then you might want to see where the journey began in the first book to feature Louisa's adventures: Vanilla Extract.

Follow her as she begins her journey through the ups and downs of dating and what starts as a curiosity exercise begins to define her future.

Available in paperback at £7.99 from: bookshop.3ppublishing.co.uk or in Kindle from Amazon.

Louisa Berry lives in Hertfordshire with her four children. While not on 'Mum-duties,' she works full time in Finance in Canary Wharf, London.

CINNAMON TWIST

CINNAMON TWIST